DATE DUE

SAND IN THE BAG

And Other Folk Stories of Ohio, Illinois, and Indiana

illustrations by John Moment

SAND IN THE BAG

And Other Folk Stories of Ohio, Indiana, and Illinois

by M. A. JAGENDORF
Author of "New England Bean Pot," etc.

introduction by WILLIAM T. UTTER

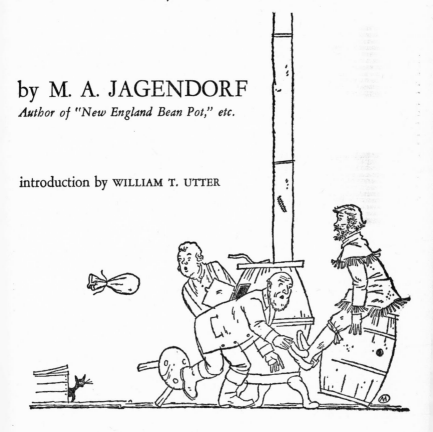

THE VANGUARD PRESS, INC. New York

To

My Wife

BOOKS BY M. JAGENDORF

PROSE

The Marvelous Adventures of Johnny Darling
New England Bean-Pot
Upstate Downstate: Folk Stories of the Middle Atlantic States
The Merry Men of Gotham
Tyll Ulenspiegel's Merry Pranks
A World of Stories for Children (IN COLLABORATION WITH
   BARRETT CLARK)
In the Days of the Han

PLAYS

Penny Puppets, Penny Theatre, and Penny Plays
One-Act Plays for Young Folks
Pantomimes for the Children's Theatre
Fairyland and Footlights
Nine Short Plays
Around America with the Indians (IN COLLABORATION WITH
   NINA B. LAMKIN)
Plays for Club, School, and Camp
Buffalmacco's Jest
The Pie and the Tart (ADAPTATIONS)
The Farce of Pierre Patelin
The Cave of Salamance
Jeppe of the Hills
The Pastrybaker

ANTHOLOGIES

Twenty-five Non-Royalty Plays for Children
Twenty-five Non-Royalty Holiday Plays
Twenty Non-Royalty Mystery Plays
Twenty Non-Royalty Ghost Plays

IN PREPARATION

Folk Stories from the Southern States
Folk Stories from the Western States

Contents

8 CONTENTS

Foreword

DR. JAGENDORF *collects stories with the feverish enthusiasm of a '49er scratching gravel for nuggets. Judging from what he shows us in this book, he had good luck out here in the Old Northwest. One might as well use the phrase the "Old Northwest," because the people of Ohio, Indiana, and Illinois object to being lumped together, or being lumped at all, so far as that goes, and yet they cannot easily deny that they were very much of a unit back in the days before statehood had divided them with artificial lines.*

There is something appropriate about the timing of this book. Ohio, celebrating one hundred and fifty years of statehood, is musing over her past; Indiana and Illinois will be in the same mood in due course. So we may as well get our stories together, along with the tools of the pioneer craftsmen and the wooden-toothed harrows of the backwoods farmers. The achievements of the collectors of folklore in this region are already quite substantial, and the results of their labors are appearing in

9

print in gratifying quantity, complete with footnotes and other scholarly paraphernalia.

Any collection of stories such as this is only half a book. The other half would be made up of the yarns the collector told in the process of bringing the old-timer to the point where he clears his throat and starts off with "That reminds me. . . ." Dr. Jagendorf is a past master at such incitement, and he could write the other part of the book if his publishers had enough paper. The style would be simple: Dr. Jagendorf would tell his yarn and then add, "I was telling this to Rigney Suggs down in Ross County and he said 'that reminds me—Did you ever hear of The Sky-Foogle of Chillicothe?' " I have seen this interchange in operation; in fact, I have been operated on and would estimate conservatively that what appears in this volume represents about one-fourth of what actually transpired.

Which reminds me that I forget to tell the Doctor a story that must have been one of the very first told in the newly created State of Ohio, a century and a half ago. The convention which framed Ohio's first Constitution had been adjourned only a few days when William Creighton, Jr., a young Chillicothe attorney, wrote to his friend Thomas Worthington: "The Sovereign People continue remarkably quiet. I must relate to you an anecdote of Daniel Hamilton. In this place the other day he was asked how the people of his neighborhood liked the Constitution. He said they did not like it at all because it had no pictures in it." Being an historian, I would have a line at the bottom of the page giving place, date, and location of the letter and might speculate in a guarded way as to whether Hamilton was a joker, a cynic, or a cynical jokester. Dr. Jagendorf, if he decided that the "nub" of the story warranted expansion, would leave no question as to Dan's point of view, nor as to how he was dressed, if that seemed important.

I looked up the word "nub" to see if I wanted it to appear above my name in print. After the definition the dictionary says "(colloq. U.S.)," and that is approval enough, but "gimmick" is not in the big book, so it must be avoided.

It is in the artful disclosure of the "nub" after a period of calculated suspense that Dr. Jagendorf excels. This must be related to the "timing" of successful comedians. At any rate, it is in the lack of this skill that an awkward story teller betrays his clumsiness. The Doctor has a clever touch. His skill is shown, too, in the carefully embellished settings which he gives his stories. It is here that one may detect the breadth of Dr. Jagendorf's own background, that he is more interested in people than in disclosing what makes a Hoosier a Hoosier—not that anyone can throw much light on the latter point.

These stories would be good currency in the Netherlands or in Wallachia. That is the advantage of having an internationalist as your story teller. I would never ask him whether the Lincoln yarn about the footprints on the ceiling was one of Tyll Eulenspiegel's merry pranks or whether someone in Languedoc ever tricked an avari-

cious landlord in the manner attributed to Tom Corwin.

The theory that every story may be traced to a proto-type surely must have its limitations. Is there any reason to believe that backwoodsmen in Illinois were less inventive, when it came to stories, than our primordial ancestors in the Grasslands to the north of the Caspian, or wherever it was that we all used to live? It is not that I object to other people carrying on the search, and I will read what they write, so long as they preserve their sense of humor. One need not subject the yarns in this volume to critical scrutiny. They were written to be enjoyed. Some I like for the "nub," some for the setting, and most of them for both.

WILLIAM T. UTTER
Denison University
Granville, Ohio

The House That Jack Built

THIS is a tale of a little mule and a big man, and a finer tale was never spun in Belmont County, in lovely Bellaire along the soft, rolling O-hi-o.

That man's name was Jacob, and they called him Jake. He was a good man, and from morn to night he worked in the mine bringing up gleaming coal in his little wheelbarrow.

From little acorns big trees grow, and Jake earned plenty of good money with his hard work.

Soon he earned so much he needed a partner to help him. Friends and relations told him to take this one and that one, men who were strong and smart, but Jake kept his counsel and said he'd think about it.

Now, Jake was wise, though he'd never gone to school. He thought of many things, and he knew the ways of men and animals.

"I'd like to find an honest partner who'll be true like a dog, not cuttin' like a buzz saw."

One day he saw a little mule, and he liked the warm,

15

wet look in his eyes. He was no more than three and a half foot high, and his coat was glossy and his little legs sturdy. He looked like a big dog, and he proved as faithful.

When Jake brought home the little animal, saying it was his partner, one and all laughed at him.

There were haw-haw's and ha-ha's.

"Who ever heard of anything so crazy. . . . A donkey for a partner! . . . Never knew wool t' grow on a donkey's hide. . . . See no white feet on that donkey to bring luck. . . . You know what they say, three things get their own way—a mule, a pig, 'n an' old woman. . . . Mule'll run you." This from the wise ones.

But Jake just smiled and said:

"This mule's goin' be my partner, an' we'll share alike work an' wealth. His name is Jack. We both got stubbornness for work, an' we're bound t' succeed."

Jake and his little mule Jack didn't waste time talking. One hacked the gleaming coal and the other pulled the loads, and both gained thereby. Hard, honest work brought hard, honest money that bought good food and kept both content. And every day and every week and every month they did more work, made more money, and were more content.

So the years rolled by while the love between the mule and Jake grew stronger and the richness grew bigger. Jake had hundreds of acres of green land and black and white painted boats on the O-hi-o. In the end he became the richest man in all Bellaire. Now folks were saying the richness came because of the little gray mule. It brought good luck and good money. But Jake smiled.

One day he called a man to build him a fine mansion.

"Put over the arch a carved head of my little four-footed helper to show one and all the beautiful things we both worked for and which we now both enjoy," Jake said. "I owe my fortune to my little partner. And no man could serve me more faithfully than did Jack."

Jack understood. There was laughter in his moist eyes, and he rubbed his nose on Jake all the time.

So the two lived happily together till the time came for them to part and meet again where they would never part.

Little Jack went first, and big Jake remained to talk about him all the time. The tale of that happy partnership spread everywhere.

I heard it and told it to you. Now you tell it to others.

Seeley Simpkins and His Bull

SAID the Blackbird to the Crow, do you know the story of Seeley Simpkins' great race in front of Norton's Mill in Mount Vernon in Ohio? Well, if you don't, you should. And you should know all about Seeley Simpkins, for he was a fine fellow who brought pleasure and laughter to all Knox County for many, many years.

No one was more welcome in cabins or frolics and hoedowns than Seeley. He blew the bugle good as Joshua and could whistle like a lark or any bird a-flying. He could croak like a frog, bark like a dog, whinny like a horse, and make the finest swill music in all of Knox County. Whenever folks gathered he played for them to dance. White folks, red folks, white children, papooses, all loved Seeley Simpkins like a brother.

Seeley Simpkins was no rich man, but he had something better—good sense in his head. He had no money to buy a horse to carry him from place to place, so what do you think he did? He bought the finest young bull in all Ohio—short, strong, and solid-built. From the time the animal was still taking milk from a wooden pail, Seeley got him used to wearing a harness. When the bull grew stronger Seeley would ride him around the pasture. In time, the two of them began traveling the roads. Up and down the roads went Seeley Simpkins on his young bull, whistling, playing music, telling funny tales to beat flying pitchforks.

When folks laughed at the rider and his steed, he would join them and add, "Ye kin keep your horses an' ye kin keep your mules, my little ridin' bull kin beat all of 'em from O-hi-o to Cali-for-ni-a."

One fine day he came to grind his corn in Norton's Mill. There folks gathered to swap tales and watch horse races. The field in front of the mill was flat and clear and just made for sports.

When Seeley Simpkins came riding on his bull, a sack of corn behind him, some fellows ready for a joke laughed and made fun of the animal and the rider.

"Yer bull looks fat an' round like a snail with short legs. Might be shown in a circus," cried one Hugh Neil.

"Guess he kin beat a snail, ef he tried hard," cried another, John Gregg by name.

But it was Tom Irwin, riding a fine horse, who laughed most at Seeley Simpkins and his bull. Soon words ran higher than treetops. Tom Irwin shouted, but Seeley Simpkins spoke as he always spoke, just a smile round his eyes and a friendly twist around the corners of his mouth.

Said Seeley: "Betch ye my bull kin beat yer horse in three shakes of a lamb's tail."

There was roaring laughter all around.

"Betch ye dollars t' corn kernels he can't."

That started an argument t' beat a hailstorm. Soon half the town was for Seeley Simpkins' bull and the other for Tom Irwin's horse. It was decided to hold the race right on the spot to see whether the bull or the horse could run better.

Stakes were put up, the judges took their places, all the townsfolk stood along the track laying bets from pocketknives to money on the bull or the horse.

Seeley Simpkins came first, astride on his little strong bull. He smiled and nodded to his friends, and his little bull snorted hard and looked around fiercely. Next came Tom Irwin on his strong, tall sorrel. The animal sure looked good but seemed kind of upset.

"Go!" the judges shouted and off they went. Folks roared, dogs barked, Indians whooped, children screamed, and Seeley Simpkins turned back and gave his little bull a hard twist at the tail.

The bull let out a roaring bellow, pawed the ground hard, and went on faster than greased lightning in a hurry. With his leaping wildcat jumps, he was eating up ground on that racecourse, now and then looking behind to see if Tom Irwin's horse was after him. You should have heard the clangoring and hollering, the bellowing and booming of the crowd. The air was torn to pieces by it.

Tom Irwin's fine horse couldn't understand what it was all about. The shouting and the roaring, the whooping and the barking frightened the animal clear out of its skin. It reared on its hind legs, stood on its forelegs, plunged forward, ran a bit, stopped, ran again, reared again . . . while Seeley Simpkins' bull was far ahead and soon passed where the judges stood—the winner of the race!

A bull had beaten a horse sure as shooting, and the crowd was shouting cannon balls.

Seeley Simpkins loved his little bull more than ever after that race. He rode him up and down the roads of Knox County, whistling, singing, making merry, and bringing more pleasure to folks than a million dollars.

The Wooing of
Lottie Moon

IN Oxford, Ohio, once upon a time there lived a girl, Charlotte Moon by name, and there was not another like her in all the land. She could ride a horse faster than a wind tearing through the branches, she had no fear of anything walking or creeping, and she was quicker with her tongue than Mike Fink with his trigger. Besides, she had a will stronger than wildcats, and most of the time she had everything pretty much her own sweet way.

When the stagecoach came clattering into Oxford, Lott 'd jump on the driver's seat, pull the horn from the driver's hand, and blow it loud enough to bring down the walls of Jericho. She could imitate man and beast to frighten bats from their hiding place. Altogether, she made more to-do in that Ohio town than Lake Erie on a stormy night. There are stories without end told about Lottie in Oxford town, and in all the South as well, but to my mind the best of all is the story of how she was wooed and won.

Lottie was no belle with blue eyes and curly hair, but

in her own sweet fashion she was a belle just the same. She was small and slender, and strong as a young sapling. Her eyes were sparkling, and her hair thick brown. Boys buzzed around her like bees around a sugar lump. She sure was no witch, but she had a witching way with 'em. Fact is, she had more suitors than a mother rabbit has bunnies. Every one of those young boys spoke of marrying, but all Lottie wanted was a gay time full of fun and frolic.

Once she went visiting some friends, and there she met young, dashing Ambrose Burnside, who later was a commander in the Union Army. He fell in love with that fickle girl the same as all the other boys and soon proposed and begged her to name the "good day."

"Any day is a good day for me," was her pert reply.

The day was set, the wedding guests came from far and near. The house was festive, and the odor of fine food was wafted from the kitchen.

Charlotte and Ambrose stood before the minister, and parents and friends were all around 'em.

"Do you take this woman to be your lawfully wedded wife?" said the minister solemnly to Ambrose.

Young Ambrose, with bright and eager face, said quickly, "I do."

"And do you, Charlotte Moon, take this man as your lawfully wedded husband?" the minister said to Lottie.

"No siree, Bob, I won't," the girl snapped back, all flushed, with laughter in her voice.

There was a hue and cry of much hurt pride, but it didn't do any good at all. Lottie just said Ambrose had asked her to name "the good day," and all days were good to her. And when Lottie said something, you could build brick mansions on it.

So she went her merry way, always making promises to young suitors and always jilting them and having more fun than a young filly in a field of spring clover.

At one time she was promised and engaged to twelve young fellows at the same time, and she ran around with a dozen besides, amongst them young Jimmy Clark, a bright, promising lawyer.

Now, Lottie's father didn't like his daughter's carryings on and often told her she'd end by staying a dried-up old maid.

"I can marry any fellow in the County and in all the State," she snapped back sharply.

"I'm not so sure, daughter. Maybe you can marry that Yankee, Ambrose Burnside, but you can't marry Jimmy Clark—he's too smart for you."

Just to show her father that she could, she soon had Jimmy at her feet, and it didn't take long for the marriage date to be set. Friends and rivals warned Jimmy and reminded him of what had happened to young Burnside.

"I'll take care o' that," Jimmy Clark replied.

The wedding day came, and a lovely day it was. Guests and relatives, ministers and music all were there ready for the festivity.

The bride, dressed beautifully in white, and the groom, handsome in black, met on the stairs, and Jimmy took Lottie's warm little hand to lead her down to the parlor for the ceremony. He looked at her lovingly, for she was lovely to look at, and he felt heaven had come to earth. As they walked down the stairs, Jimmy suddenly thought of Ambrose Burnside.

He put his left hand on his pocket and whispered into Lottie's little ear:

"Darling, I have a pistol here in my pocket. There'll be a wedding here today or a funeral here tomorrow."

Little Lottie turned red to her ears, but she never said a word—until she sweetly said, "I do."

It was a grand wedding that day for Jimmy Clark and Lottie Moon, and they lived a happy, full-of-arguments life ever after.

The Tapping Ghost of Edinburg

IN Edinburg, not far from Tallmadge in Ohio, there was a ghost that frightened young and old. Young folks spoke of it with shivers in the spine, and old, with voices hushed and low. The ghost lived in a house just a little to the south of the town square, and everyone kept away from that spot at night like from a rattlesnake with bells on.

The family that had lived in that house had all died, and since it was a very old house and battered down, with a leaking roof, no one wanted to buy it. Nobody wanted to buy the house with a ghost that walked around at night going tap, tap, tap all the time.

Sometimes that tapping was slow and dragging-like, sometimes fast and leaping-like, as if after something in a hurry. The first tap, tap, tapping had been heard by some small boys of the town. It was on a cold day, and they had been playing and gone into the old house to warm themselves. The wind was blowing through the broken windows, and it was really colder there than

26

outside. They had just made up their minds to go, when they heard the tap, tapping followed by a sound that was between a squeak and a whistle. The four boys, frightened white, all ran and told it to their parents.

The parents told it to their neighbors, the neighbors told it to their friends and relatives, and before the evening was over the whole town knew there was a tapping ghost in the deserted house, and everybody was scared good and proper. Fear travels quicker than lightning. The news of the tapping ghost in Edinburg traveled as far as Tallmadge, and folks came from over there, frightened to death to see that haunted house. They'd just step in for a few seconds, run out shivering, and swear they had heard the tapping.

It was wintertime then, and the roads were just one bump after another, but so many came in sleighs to hear that tapping ghost they wore the bumps in the road smooth 's a rail.

Everybody said that the terrible ghost in the deserted house was a visitation on the town.

Now, one drop of sense 's worth a thousand pounds of fear, and there were three fellows in Edinburg who had that drop of sense. These three just didn't believe in ghosts and said the tapping wasn't done by any ghost at all. They would prove it by staying in the deserted house one night and find out the real cause of that noise.

Folks said they were foolhardy and would be sorry for their deed. But the three laughed and said they'd soon be laughing at all the town.

On a quiet night when the moon shone white, the three, dressed in wool and with boots to keep warm, went to the deserted house. They made no fire, and each hid in a different room to catch that tapping ghost. Each could see into the parlor, from which the tapping came. They waited, eyes and ears wide open.

The cold, silvery moon shone clear in the sky, and there was a world full of stars in the heavens. The empty rooms were still as a Christmas night. Even the shadows didn't move.

Suddenly the three saw something black and white and furry moving . . . limping . . . tap, tap, tap. Each time it moved it came down with a tapping thud.

It was a cat!

But witches have been known to turn into cats ever since witches have been. This limping cat might be a witch in disguise!

The three, a little shivery now and mouths a little dry, watched the animal.

The cat went tapping, tapping along the wall. Then it stopped in a shadow and stood there as if frozen to the ground. Only its eyes shone like jewels from far India.

So they all stood silently. The three fearless fellows and the black and white cat, all *s t a r i n g*.

Suddenly a small, thick, dark something came scuttling from out of the wall. The black-and-white cat leaped in the air, then came down with a thud on the scuttling something! There was a squealing whistle and the black-and-white cat went off quickly, tap, tap, tap, tap.

The cat had caught the mouse.

The three fellows laughed till the tears ran down their faces.

Cried one: "The ghost in the deserted house is a cat, one leg shorter than the others, catching mice!"

Cried the other: "I know that cat—it lost one leg when it was caught in a trap. Each time it limps, it comes down with a tapping thud."

Cried the third: "Fear's smaller than a fly, but it hits harder than an elephant."

The three laughed, all Edinburg laughed over their silly scare, and here's hoping they have laughed at fear ever since.

The Tale of Tom Corwin

WHEN you talk of great men in Ohio, you sure must speak of Tom Corwin. Tom Corwin was born and bred in the Buckeye State, and he was big, burly, and dark, and smart enough to go to Congress to help rule our land.

There are a thousand stories running loose like eels in oil about Tom Corwin, about the things he said and the things he did, and here is one of them that has brought good laughter for many a year to Ohio firesides.

One day, Tom Corwin and a friend traveling to the Capitol stopped at an inn that was run by an innkeeper who'd cheat a pig of its tail.

That innkeeper was so crooked he couldn't fall down a well. He had made up with the coach driver, who was cut from the same skin, that when the driver came by early in the morning to pick up travelers, he'd blow his horn, shout he was in a hurry, and start up quick as a wink. This way, those eating their breakfast had to stop before they were done but would have to pay just the same. Of course, the innkeeper gained money from that, and he gave the coach driver his share.

Tom Corwin knew this and made up his mind to teach the two thieves a good lesson they wouldn't forget.

He and his friend rested for the night, arose in the morning, and sat down for breakfast with the rest of the guests. They weren't halfway through when the coach dashed up, the bugle sounded, and the driver roared he was in a hurry with the mail and would start at once.

The eating guests rose pell-mell, dropping spoons, leaving food on the table, and rushing off for baggage and seats. All but Tom Corwin and his friend, who knew all about the scheme. They kept on eating as the room emptied and the landlord went out collecting money for bed and breakfast.

No sooner was he out than Corwin quickly picked up the spoons lying around, put them into the coffeepot, and covered it.

The innkeeper returned and saw the two sitting at the table.

"Gentlemen, you still here!" he cried. "The coach is going, you'll be left behind. Run, you still might catch him!"

"We are in no hurry, host," Tom Corwin said quietly. "It's a good breakfast and we'd like to finish it. But, good man, would you please furnish us some spoons? There are none here."

"Spoons!" the landlord cried, looking all over the table and his eyes growing big as saucers. "Spoons! Where are the spoons? I put them out. There were spoons. . . ."

"Good host, so there were," said Tom Corwin, "but when the driver began shouting 'hurry,' and everyone rushed, I think I saw someone picking up those spoons. I don't remember just who."

The innkeeper turned red with fury. He rushed out as if a horde of hornets were after him, leaped on a horse without a saddle, and took after the coach.

When he caught up, he shouted for the driver to return and help him find the thief who stole the spoons. Someone in that coach had stolen them and put them in a bag.

The coach turned back, the grumbling, swearing passengers got off with their baggage, and the innkeeper began searching for the spoons which he said someone had stolen.

When nothing was found, the angry passengers got on the coach again to the tune of the cursing innkeeper and the angry driver. Tom Corwin and his friend were done with their breakfast by then. Both came up to the door where the host was standing and paid for their food and bed. Said Tom Corwin, smiling broadly:

"Host, here is your money. I am sorry to see you in bad humor, and, now that I think of it, I didn't see anyone putting the spoons in their traveling bags, but I think someone put them into the coffeepot. Perhaps next time, if you'll let the guests peacefully finish their breakfasts for which they pay you, there'll be less excitement and the spoons will be left on the table. You know what happened to the jackass that tried to get horns—he came back with long ears."

The rogue innkeeper was no fool and understood; whether or not he changed no one could tell me. But let us think well of him and say he did.

That is the kind of tale they tell about Tom Corwin in Ohio.

The Faithful Dog

THERE are tales without end about faithful dogs all over the world, and Ohio has its share of them. This is one told in Freedom township in Portage County.

In the early days, when Freedom township had no more than a dozen families, there was amongst them a man named Warner Durkee. He was a famous hunter, though ill in health. For Warner Durkee was the kind who gain strength of body from strength of will.

One day he went off hunting, followed by his dog, who was always at his side. He went through paths and brambles, woods and jackbrush, looking for game. The sun was pretty low when he caught sight of a deer, and he and his dog began following it swiftly. The long day without rest and the running after the deer was perhaps too much for Warner's strength, for all of a sudden he began to feel dizzy and weak. He stopped and sat down on the ground. No sooner did he sit down than he began bleeding from his mouth, and though he tried his best to stop it, he could not.

34

The dog watched his master and showed great distress and worry. He ran back and forth and around him. He barked and whined; stopped, looked at him, opened his mouth wide as if to say something, and then started all these things over again. Warner knew his dog, for he loved the animal as folk often do, and in between the spurting of the blood he said to the dog, part in jest, part earnest, and part sadly:

"Run home and tell 'em I'm bleedin' t' death. Run quick and save me!"

The animal seemed to understand his master's words. He went off like an arrow, barking loudly.

Soon he reached the little settlement and ran right to the cabin where his master lived with his family. Those inside were asleep without worrying. It was not uncommon for Warner to go hunting and stay out all night.

The dog barked wildly at the door; he got on his hind feet and scratched savagely on the wood, keeping up his howling. It awoke Warner's son. He opened the door to let the animal in, figured his father was not far behind, and went back to bed. But the dog kept up his wild behavior. He barked and howled and tore at the sheets and woke all the family. He was told to lie down, he was driven off, he was even offered food, but nothing seemed to interest him. Fact is, he was getting worse. Suddenly he ran to the leather trousers lying on a bench, pulled them, and tugged them to the door. The family began to understand that the dog meant something more by all that wildness. Warner's son put on his clothes, and the dog howled seemingly with joy, running all the time to the door. Young Durkee followed.

The faithful animal ran ahead wildly, stopped, turned around to see if he were followed, and then ran ahead again. So the two went through woods and brush until they reached the place where Warner Durkee was lying on the ground, too weak to speak or raise himself. He was still bleeding from the mouth.

His son lifted him, raised him on his shoulders, and slowly went homeward. The dog ran before and around them, barking joyfully and seeming to understand that his master was safe now.

And so a faithful dog saved his master's life. Soon Warner became well again, and dog and master were more inseparable than ever.

Smart Sam'l Dany

SAM'L DANY of Crawford County in Ohio was smart enough to make crows laugh.

One day Sam'l Dany went a-huntin', went in the woods to shoot deer, but it wasn't Sam'l Dany's huntin' day, same as no other day was.

He tramped 'round and 'round the woods till every creature knowed Sam'l Dany was out a-huntin', so they cropped grass and walked 'round him 'sted of before 'm.

Deer and fox, hare an' bear, frolicked all 'round, but Sam'l Dany saw 'em no more than if he had pun'kin eyes.

"What's the use o' huntin' when there ain't no game 'round?" He sat and ate his bread and meat.

The wood creatures lay a-restin', too, there was a still zoomin' in the dark woods, and Sam'l thought it a good time for stealin' a wink o' sleep. So he laid him down on the good earth and soon was dreamin' of angels bringin' sizzlin' deer his way.

When the sun was gettin' low and the wind was blowin' warm, he got up.

"Time's ripe fer goin' home an' fer the evenin' meal. Night huntin' ain't no good fer a Christian man."

He set one foot afore the other, his nose straight in front the way t' home.

The more he walked, the more he seemed to walk. There was no end to that walkin', and he was no nearer to home. 'Twas gettin' darker all the time.

"I'm lost, sure's cookin'," cried Sam'l Dany, and he began shoutin' and runnin' and shoutin' and runnin'. But with all the shoutin' and runnin' he didn't seem to get any nearer to home. He was gettin' all tuckered out and near cryin', for 'twas now near dark all over the place.

All at once he saws signs pointin' to a farm, felt a foot-path under his feet, felt broken branches like made by passin' cattle. Sure 'nuf, there was a barn risin' out of the twilight, with buckets and wheelbarrows out-side. He saw a chicken house with a door hangin' loose, a cabin with chinks wide open, and a broken fence. Looked kind o' familiar.

A woman in a calico dress was standin' at the fence lookin' anxious all 'round.

"Good even', good woman," cried Sam'l Dany. "Know this neck o' the woods?"

"Know it good 's the palm o' my hand."

"Know perhaps where Sam'l Dany's cabin is?"

"Know it good 's the face in my head."

"Know Sam'l Dany?"

"Know 'm fer the biggest, silliest fellow in all O-hi-o."

"Can y' tell me where his cabin is?"

"Lan' sakes! Knew you were a fool, Sam'l Dany, but didn't know y' were such a big fool not t' know yer own home an' wife."

"Comin' t' think of it, this is my own cabin, an' you're my own wife that's a-talkin' t' me. I'm mighty glad t' find ye, for I'd lost my way an' sure thought I'd have t' sleep in the dark woods the night long. 'Deed the good Lord 's kind t' me."

Sam'l Dany was happy as a cricket in a chimney. He went into his cabin, had mush and milk for supper, and slept with a clear conscience.

Now don't y' think Sam'l Dany was smart 'nuf to make crows laugh?

The Sad Tale of Three Slavers

ONCE three slavers were hunting for slaves who were fleeing to gain their freedom, and thereby hangs a tale.

One sweet Sunday, in Bloomfield in Ohio, when folks were coming from praying to the Lord, they saw a sad sight. On the North Pike going from Warren to Ashtabula there came stumbling along, falling and running, a young Negro and his wife and two children. They were slaves fleeing from their masters so they would not be separated, for they had heard they would each be sold to different owners.

Bloomfield's folks stopped, looked, shook their heads sadly, and felt sorry that man had to flee from man to live in peace. They cried to them good luck and God-speed. Some even gave them coppers. And when the good townspeople were eating their noonday meal they all thought and hoped the fugitives would reach safety and security.

Just as the sun was setting in gold, there came rushing into town a-horseback three men—father, son, and friend

—out on the hunt for the fleeing slaves. They looked in houses, went through fields, asked this one and that one and everyone if they hadn't seen a strapping young Negro, a strong young Negro woman, and two well-built children fleeing from their rightful owners.

Folks in Bloomfield had little love for slaveowners and slave hunters and said they hadn't seen them.

But when the slave owners came to the inn of the town they heard a different tale.

The innkeeper, Joshua, loved slavers as snakes love boiling water. He was a mighty smart fellow who always liked a clever trick, and while the slavers were firing questions at him he had an idea that would beat a fox early in the morning.

"Bless ye, gentlemen," he said, sugar on his face, "bless ye, 'deed I saw the four fleeing slaves. Exactly as ye describe 'em. They were on the road to Ashtabula. They were crawlin' sorefooted like snails and they can't be very far. They just can't escape ye, an' night is comin' on fast and it'll be pitch black. Best thing is to wait for the morning. Ye've got plenty o' time. I'll wake ye early. Might as well stay in my inn, enjoy a good meal cheaply, and take a well-needed rest. Ye'll sure get those wool-heads tomorrow."

The host was so honey-kind, and the slavers were so tired and hungry, they decided to stay.

The three gentleman slave hunters ate well, drank well, and soon were dreaming of the slaves caught in the morning sunlight. But as for the host, he was wide awake and at work.

First thing he did was call his servants one after the other and tell 'em to sleep the next morning a little later and to make as little noise as possible when they got up.

"Just don't get up till ye hear me," he said. Some looked puzzled, some knowing, but all promised faithfully to obey.

Then, with a pleased smile on his face, he ran to the house of his friend Barnes the blacksmith and told him what he had in mind. Barnes roared at the scheme, slapped his thighs, and cried he was with it body, boots, and britches.

"Just you hide horseshoes and nails and make yourself scarce tomorrow morn. Keep the smithy door locked till I find ye."

Next he ran to his neighbor, Squire Brown, and told him the scheme. Squire Brown laughed with glee, cried hallelujah!, and said it was the slickest and funniest scheme since America began and swore he'd do all he could to help.

As soon as Joshua went, Squire Brown hitched up his covered wagon and went where he believed the fleeing slaves had gone. Bloomfield and all the towns nearby were honeycombed with homes where slaves were hidden. He rode about twelve miles till he came to a house where he knew slaves often found refuge.

He knocked on the door and told his errand, but it took heaps of talk before he could take the slaves with him. Off he went in a gallop and soon had 'em safe in a barn not far from Bloomfield.

Squire Brown went home feeling warm with pleasure for having a share in the good act.

As for Joshua, he was still busy in the stable arranging everything just right for the slavers.

The morning came warm and sunny, birds were singing, pigeons were cooing, and hens were scratching, but there wasn't a sound of bustling in the inn as there always was at that time of the day. It was quiet as a mole run.

The sun kept on shining stronger and was beating in the room where the slavers were sleeping. In the end it woke 'em, and they leaped out o' bed like burnt, for they could tell by the sun it was late in the morning. They roared for the innkeeper and shouted at him why he hadn't awakened 'em early as he said he would. Joshua ran in half dressed, cried in distress, begged to be forgiven, and swore at his help who were lazy and ever oversleeping. He ran through the house as if he had lost his head, but soon the morning meal was on the table, and a good meal it was. The coffee smelled strong, and the mistress of the inn was very pleasant, urging the three gentlemen slavers to eat and drink. Soon they forgot their anger. There were second helpings and second cups of coffee. At last they were done.

"Guess I better get your horses ready," said Joshua.

"Ain't gotten 'em ready yet! Jumpin' Johnny! Put wings on yer feet. You should've gotten 'em ready while we were eatin'."

" 'Tain't often we have such fine guests in our inn," the hostess said while her husband ran out. "Don't blame my husband, gentlemen."

The slavers smiled and went out to the stable, where they found Joshua ranting and roaring.

"Where's the key! Where is that key? Where is it? Ye see, gentlemen, I always lock the stable door at night for fear o' thieves. Now I can't find the key. Maybe I dropped it."

He bent down, looking in the dirt and in the grass. So did the help and the hostess and the slavers.

Suddenly Joshua leaped and shouted: "Shucks creation! Now I remember. I left the key over the fireplace."

He ran into the inn and soon came out holding the key in his hand. The door was unlocked, and there they found that each horse wanted a shoe and one of the animals had a cracked hoof.

"Wife," cried the innkeeper, "this is my black morning. Everything's gone wrong. Gentlemen, I must beg yer forgiveness. I must help ye now. Come, let's rush to Barnes the blacksmith. He's a friend o' mine, and I'll make 'm stop all work and tend to yer horses."

He rushed off with the horses, the slavers following. Soon they got to Barnes the smith, and—the door was locked! Joshua banged, shouted, used strong words, but it didn't bring the smith.

A crowd gathered around 'em, but not a one knew where Barnes was.

"I'll run and find that nimshi," cried Joshua, and off he went.

The horses pawed the ground, and the slavers shouted black words and walked up and down, while folks standing around smiled and said little. They kind o' guessed what the game was.

It took near half an hour until Joshua returned with Barnes, and then—the smith found something had gone wrong with the lock. It took a long time before that door was opened.

Now there was new trouble: making a fire.

"It's the first time in my life such a thing's happened to me," the smith kept on mumbling.

At last the fire was ready, and now Barnes found there wasn't a single horseshoe and not a nail in the smithy. So he set to work making both.

The hours dragged on, the slavers were wild 's a hurricane on Lake Erie, and folk standing around smiled and kept their mouths buttoned up.

The sun was standing in the middle o' the sky, but Barnes was still hammering and pounding. His hands seemed made o' bullet lead that day. At last the horses were ready and the slavers rode off wilder than hungry wolves.

They rushed in the direction Joshua and the others told 'em. They rode wild as Indians, passing right alongside the barn where the slaves were hiding.

When they were gone, Squire Brown came for the

fugitives and put 'em in a hut on his own grounds where they would be safe until the catawampus was over.

Three days later, three tired slavers came back to Bloomfield—without any slaves. At once the sheriff took 'em in tow and told 'em they hadn't paid the right toll when they passed through the town and would now have to pay a five-dollar fine.

The slavers cried and shouted, but to the judge they had to go. No innkeeper would lodge their horses, so they tied 'em to a signpost and went to pay the fine.

While they were gone some boys, or maybe older ones full of old scratch, cut off chunks from the horses' manes and tails so they looked silly 'nuf to stop a clock.

When the slavers saw that, they called Bloomfield the devil's own pasture and many more names like that and ran off as quick as they could.

But folks laughed at this. All except Squire Brown, who held out that the horses' manes and tails should not have been cut and shorn, for there was no sense in punishing fine animals for the misdeeds of their masters—and I say the same.

A Little Story About a Great Man

JOHN Brown's body lies a mold'ring in the grave,
John Brown's body lies a mold'ring in the grave,
John Brown's body lies a mold'ring in the grave,
But his soul goes marching on.

So the old song goes, and I know you have heard it
and have sung it. And you have heard of John Brown,
too, with the long, thin face and the square, long beard;
great John Brown of Harper's Ferry fame, who wanted
to see all men, black and white, free and equal. You have
heard tell of the bloody battles he fought for what he
believed was right and of how he died without fear, for
the "noble cause of freedom." But folks tell other kinds
of tales about him, too. Tales warm like spinning rain in a
thunderstorm. You'll hear such tales around Hudson,
where John Brown came when he was only five years
old, and now I'll tell you one of them.

One day, when he was still a little fellow, he did a deed
he hadn't ought to have done and for which he deserved

to be punished. Father Brown did not believe in sparing the rod, and he used it well, but never in the house—only in the barn. In the house there was peace, no punishment. After John had done what he shouldn't, his father said to him: "I'll see you in the barn soon as I am finished with the chores." Then he went on sawing a log.

Johnny, innocent-like, walked behind the house, but when he was out of sight of his father he turned and immediately went through the back door into the barn.

Now, there was one special spot there where Father Brown taught his young ones the right way of living, and to that place Johnny quickly went. Right near was a shallow place under the floor made to store farm tools. John lifted the planks, took away the supports, and reset the boards, so that anyone stepping there would fall right through, a little over two feet, onto the pile of tools lying underneath. Then he went back into the house.

When Father Brown was finished sawing the logs he told John he'd see him in the barn. John went there, his little longish face in solemn silence. His father followed.

First John tried to tell his father he did not mean to do what he had done, then he said he'd never do it again, but the father said the best way to remember doing right is to drive out doing wrong with a switch.

John took off his coat, turned about, ready to be punished; but the moment John's father raised his arm high, the boy leaped across the planks he had loosened. Father Brown followed quickly, stepped on the planks and—

crack! went through the floor right onto the handles of scythes and hayforks, without any hurt, while John ran out back to the house.

Strangely, Owen Brown did not punish his son for what he had done. Perhaps he thought his son had a right to do what he did, if he had the right to whip him for it. I don't really know why, and the story does not tell. But what I do know is that little John did not feel the least sorry for it.

When John Brown grew to be a man, he remembered the whippings his father had given him and remembered, too, how he had tried to escape punishment. Often, after he punished his own children with the switch, he'd give the switch to the one punished and turn about and say: "Now you do the same to me, for your bad behavior may be the fault of my improper teaching."

This is one of the many stories about John Brown, whose greater story tells about his battle for freedom and justice.

A Deer Trick

SAMMY EDWARDS, a great hunter of Ohio, could spin yarns better than a squirrel could crack nuts. But the best of all the tales he tells is what happened to him when he was still a young one running loose like a frisky calf.

First he and his folks lived in Cincinnati. There Sammy and his younger brother George, two nimble and sharp little fellows, learned clever tricks and sleight of hand. They learned them from men who showed such tricks at fairs and earned some coppers for their pains. Soon they were so good at it, their young friends and even older ones thought the two had magic power.

They could make a handkerchief vanish in the air like a papery cloud in the sky. They both could throw a stone swift as a bullet and straight as an arrow and bring down a squirrel or maybe even a rabbit with it. And they learned a clever trick to hide the stones so good you could only see their arms move, and, bang! an animal was down. Everyone was sure it was done by magic.

After a time they moved to Piquay County. Sammy was then twelve years old, and his brother George, ten. When they came to the new place they showed off their tricks even more than they had in Cincinnati. Piquay Bay was then a little settlement, and quickly these two boys were more famous than a flying horse. Folks even called them witches, particularly the Pennsylvania Dutchmen who lived there and believed more in the power of witches than in the ways of the Lord.

Not only did these two little scalawags always brag of the tricks they could do, but they also boasted of tricks they couldn't do. One time they said they could even turn themselves into deer and run so fast no hound could ever catch 'em.

Young and old listened with eyes and ears wide open and feared them, though they were only little acorns. They believed the two had great power to do good or harm.

One time some men came to hire them to drive off the birds and squirrels that were eating the corn in their fields. It did little good for the boys' mother to say that her sons were just clever tricksters and could not do any hexing. Those folks thought the woman was only unneighborly and cantankerous.

Soon after, Sammy and George went to a vendue, where folks came to buy and sell, to eat and drink, and to gossip and frolic. The two showed all the tricks they knew. Handkerchiefs flew away; swinging arms and hands brought down all sorts of things a ways off. They could make nuts disappear and perform many other magic acts.

A great crowd gathered round 'em, watching. In the end, twenty Pennsylvania Dutchmen said they'd each give them a dollar if the boys would turn themselves into deer as they said they could.

Sammy and George were ashamed to tell they had been bragging, so they said they'd show 'em this wonder, but first they'd have to go into the woods to speak the proper magic words.

"Then we'll come out like deer," Sammy said, " 'n you'll see us run so fast nothin' can catch us, not even the fastest runnin' hound."

Every mother's son believed the two little devilkins.

Sammy and George ran off into the woods, figuring they would run home from there and let those beanheads who didn't know it was only bragging burn their noses in the Ohio sun.

Now, it so happened that these two little snipper-snappers had more luck than the fellow that was thrown into Lake Erie and came up with a fish in his mouth. Just when they were running away, two deer a nearby farmer kept for his and his children's pleasure got out from their pen and were running loose. Dogs, smelling their tracks, raced after 'em, and the two frightened animals, not knowing where to turn, ran right through the market place where the vendue was being held. They fled past the crowd of men who had offered the money to the boys if they turned themselves into deer. And these muttonheads fully believed the tame deer were the two boys turned into beasts. From that day on Sammy and George were thought the most famous witches in Piquay County, and the two made hay while the sun shone bright.

Those were the kind of witches folks found in the Buckeye State.

The Sky-Foogle of Chillicothe

THERE is no town along the banks of the Scioto by a bear's tail-wagging like Chillicothe. Ask any Chillicothean and he'll tell you that is so. It was there they had the "Salt Sea Crab's Club" to which the finest men belonged; and there they had the "Pallbearers Association," the like there was not in all Ohio; and there they had the "Sky-Foogle," the like there never was in all these United States.

The Sky-Foogle was a beast no man had ever captured, no man had ever seen. He was more terrible than the wild lions of the West—too terrible to be even described in speaking words.

Now, in those days there lived a printer man in Chillicothe named Shriner. He was a Pennsylvania Dutchman, a most valiant man, and very secretive. One day he said to himself, "I'll catch that Sky-Foogle beast and make him help me earn some money."

Without whispering a word to man or minister he watched and waited and waited and watched, and as he

waited and watched and watched and waited, a scheme
to catch that terrible beast grew clear in his mind. And
in good time . . . he caught the Sky-Foogle.

He put it in chains and hid it in the dark, and he hired
a hall so that his fellow Chillicotheans could see that
terror of the earth and sky. Then he set the day for the
great event. Chillicotheans young and old came from
near and far, and all paid good money to see the ferocious
Sky-Foogle.

All filed into the big hall and sat silently on the hard
benches. There was plenty of hard swallowing and no
tongue wagging. Time dragged on and the minutes
seemed like long winter nights. Suddenly there came
from behind the stage a fierce growling. Then a great
roaring and terrible cries and screams. Men and women,
boys and girls turned white, and teeth chattered so you
could hear them a mile off. All were paralyzed with fear.

Then Mister Shriner bounded on the stage, his clothes
all torn, his hair disheveled, and the fear of Judgment
Day on his face.

"Run for your lives! Save yourselves!" he screamed.
"The terrible Sky-Foogle has escaped." That crowd
flew out faster than greased lightning. Not a one thought
of demanding the money he had paid to see the beast.

Soon hall and street were deserted. Everyone was
gone, even valiant Shriner the printer.

As the hours passed and fear fled from the first capital
of Ohio, folks came out from house and home, where
they had been hiding, and spoke to one another once

again. First thing, they looked for Shriner, but there was no sign or smoke of him. Some said the Sky-Foogle had devoured him and died from it, and others said other things, but no one ever questioned whether Shriner the printer caught that terrible beast.

To this day, on stormy nights, when whistling snows and wild winds blow through the streets of Chillicothe, good Chillicotheans tell the story of the terrible Sky-Foogle and Shriner the valiant printer.

The Immortal J.N.

STRANGE men of Ohio have often been the great men of Ohio. That is, folks thought them strange for doing things different from what others did. There was Johnny Appleseed, who walked through Ohio giving rich fruit and rich kindness so that all loved him. And there was Immortal J.N. Free, who also went through Ohio, taking many things instead of giving, but he did it so graciously and so much like a great lord that folks liked him just the same.

He was a queer man, Immortal J.N., as he was called. His name was Free, and freely he took everything that came his way.

Whatever he did, he did different from others. When he wrote a card to a friend he put down the name and next to it "and esteemable lady" though the man never had a wife. He'd write the message across the card like all other folk, and when he'd get to the bottom, he'd turn it around and begin writing whatever more he had to say across what he had already written. You couldn't read that post card no more than you could read birds' tracks on a porch.

He'd gather great bundles of newspapers, tie them with strings, and throw them off the trains when he rode through the town. He never paid for riding on a train. The railroad presidents decided it was wiser and cheaper to let him ride without paying than haul him to court, pay lawyers, and waste time arguing about it.

He said that he'd never die, and that is why folks called him "Immortal." And die he never will in Ohio as long as stories of olden days are told.

Now, one time Immortal J.N. had been riding on a train and not paying a penny, as was his habit. He got off at the town where he wanted to go and walked along the street like a great lord. 'Deed, he looked like a lord. He was a tall man, straight as an arrow, walking with a long, free stride. He had dark eyes sharp as an eagle's, and his long, black hair hung down his shoulders like a lion's mane. Folks greeted him, and he had a kind word for everyone in fine language like one who had read books. So he came to an inn where he meant to stay for a while.

He remained there three days and visited friends. He looked into the schoolrooms where teachers were teaching children, telling the teacher he was satisfied with their discipline, adding: "The pressure on me is very heavy today." This was his way of saying he was not feeling well.

Now, the hotel man knew all about Immortal J.N.'s

habit of not paying his bills, but he thought himself a mighty slick squirrel who would make him pay for once.

So the time passed pleasantly until the day when Immortal J.N. told the innkeeper he was ready to leave. Men who were sitting around near the inn were arguing and even making bets whether the innkeeper 'd get money out of the famous man, or whether he would fare no better than all the others who had tried and failed. It was almost as good as watching horses run.

"You're goin', Mister Free?" the innkeeper said when he saw him coming down the stairs.

"That I am, my good man, and I was very pleased with your fine inn, and I will tell all my friends about it. I wish you a happy day, for I must be off."

"Haven't you forgotten something, Mister Free?" the innkeeper said, while those around listened with ears wide open.

"As far as I know, sir, I have not forgotten anything."

"I fear you have, Mister Free. You have forgotten to pay."

"I never pay bills, sir. I paid them when I was a rich man and had money. But I lost it all, millions, in the West, raising horses. Then I amassed a fortune once again, and lost it when I tried to bring water to my mines out West. Since then I feel the good country owes me money, and so I never pay bills."

"I can't help it if you lost your money, Mister Free. Here folks pay their bills, and I expect you to do the same, sir."

"My friend," Immortal J.N. said, "I never pay bills anywhere. No one ever asks me for them."

The innkeeper began all over again. He raised his voice, he begged, he threatened, but Immortal J.N. kept calm, spoke quietly but firmly, and said he would not pay. Then the innkeeper came out with an idea he had thought of and which he was sure would give him at least some of the money.

"Mister Free," said he, "I will show you I can act like a gentleman. I will cut the bill in half. If you pay just one half, I'll drop the other half."

An even more pleasant smile came to Immortal J.N.'s face. He bowed his head a little and said:

"I never would permit any man to outdo me in generosity. If you, sir, are gentlemanly enough to throw off half of my bill, I will be equally generous and throw off the other half as far as Lake Erie." Then he walked out, head high, smiling, and bidding good-by to all those present.

And those present told the innkeeper not to be too angry, for if railroad presidents allowed Immortal J.N. to travel free on their roads, surely an innkeeper should allow that famous Ohioan to stay free in his inn.

The Boy Who Would Be an Orator

THEY still like telling tales around Cedarville and Xenia in Ohio about "Young Whitelaw," Whitelaw Reid, who became one of the great statesmen and newspapermen of our land.

Young Whitelaw was eager to learn from his earliest days, when he ran around barefoot and went to the little red-brick schoolhouse near Cedarville. He studied hard and soon was at the head of his class, and none could beat him writing pieces. They were humdingers, and he was mighty proud of 'em. But when it came to speaking pieces, he was none too pert, and that was just what he wanted to do most of all. He wanted to speak the pieces he wrote just like the great orators of the day who held debates. But, you know, to want a thing and to be able to do it aren't the same. Much as Young Whitelaw wanted to be a speaker, he just couldn't be, for his voice wasn't made for speaking; it was very weak.

Now, Young Whitelaw loved his father and mother very much. He looked on them as much as friends as he did as parents, and one day he told them how he felt about speaking pieces.

Robert Reid was a carpenter by trade but a man who had read many good books and knew a great many things. The boy's mother was a fine pioneer woman, hard-working and ready to help friends and neighbors, and in her home folks gathered for quilting bees, for gossiping, and for talking to Robert Reid.

Both father and mother listened to young Whitelaw's complaint, and then Father Reid said:

"Son, did you ever hear about Demosthenes and d'you know who he was? If you haven't I'll tell you. Demosthenes was one of the finest orators Athens in Greece ever had, and he had great courage and always worked hard to gain his ends.

"Well, when Demosthenes was young he had just about the same ambition as you have. He also wanted to be a great orator, but he couldn't speak loud, and he had something wrong with his speech. Maybe he stuttered a little. D'you know what he did, son?"

Young Whitelaw was all eyes and ears, listening. "No I don't," he said, near breathless.

"Well, son, first he learned all about speaking from teachers, just as you do in school. Next thing, he had to make his voice strong and clear. He lived not far from the sea, so he went to the shore, picked pebbles from the sand, put 'em in his mouth, and spoke his pieces loud as he could, trying to beat the roaring sea. He kept that up for a long time, and soon he *could* speak loud enough to be heard above the sea, and his voice became clear.

"He studied history and he studied great speeches and in the end he became the greatest orator of Greece."

Jumping Junipers! From that day on there was no holding Young Whitelaw. He had no roaring ocean with pebbles, but he had a slick head on his shoulders and he thought up something good. First he took the town job of hog-an'-cow calling and taking the animals to pasture and bringing them home. He earned good money by that and gave fine exercise to his voice.

Every night you could hear his Pooooo-o-o-o Iee! Pooooo-o-o-o Iee! Pooooo-o-o-o Iee! over and over again, louder than any boy ever shouted before. And you could hear his Sooooo-o-o-o, Boss! Sooooo-o-o-o, Boss! Sooooo-o-o-o, Boss! Soo, Soo, Soo, so it would hurt your ears.

But like most young ones from the Year One, Young Whitelaw didn't get on fast enough to suit himself. He figured hog-an'-cow calling twice a day wouldn't make him a great orator as quick as he wanted to be one. So he began speaking pieces just to the wind or to the hogs and cows. He'd stand before the good fat Moley and Brindle and Jersey cows with the rich bags o' milk, waiting patiently along the flower-bordered country roadways, and shout his pieces about patriotism loud enough to be heard a mile off. Folks around hearing this began saying Young Whitelaw was a queer kind, talking to himself and to the cows and birds.

Do you think that stopped him from practicing? Not by guns and oxen. It made him work harder, until all looked at him sideways and kept out of his way. They wouldn't let him tend their hogs and cows for fear he'd put a hex on 'em, as they said in Pennsylvania.

That didn't bother Young Whitelaw a straw's worth. Next thing he did was to get up on those high mounds found around Green County and other parts of Ohio. Folks say they were built by the Mound Builders, a people that lived in America long, long before the Indians. Young Whitelaw 'd get up the top o' those mounds when he was through with school, or early in the morning before he went to school, and make believe the swallows and bobolinks in the air and the growing things and the pasturing animals were folks listening. He'd make long speeches by Daniel Webster and other great men, or maybe his own, all with motions of his hands and face.

He'd stand on the highest parts of these mounds shouting at the top of his voice, waving has hands wildly, walking up and down, and altogether acting like one that's queer in the head.

Now, the highest one of these mounds around that neighborhood belonged to Farmer Jackson, and that one was Young Whitelaw's favorite spot. Farmer Jackson didn't like this and had told Young Whitelaw to keep off his property. If he wanted to sit there he had nothing against it, but not when he was carrying on as if he had been sitting on a nest o' yellow jackets. It disturbed the animals, Farmer Jackson said.

Young Whitelaw took no heed o' that. He came there just the same, booming and bellowing his speeches. You must know that by then, practicing all the time, he could bellow like an ox and could be heard as far as Xenia.

One morning when he was on his way to school too early and passed the Jackson mound, he thought it'd be a good idea to practice a piece he had studied the night before.

Though it was quite early, Farmer Jackson was out plowing with his horses. The team was none too good, and when they suddenly heard the thundering voice coming down from on high and echoing from the nearby hills, they got scared. They stood on their hind legs and pulled the plow in all directions, nearly tearing the harness apart. Farmer Jackson tried his best gee'ing, haw'ing, and whoa'ing, but it did little good. He worked so hard the sweat ran down his face, and he shouted so loud trying to drown Young Whitelaw's roaring, he got hoarse. In the end he edged the team into the corner of the fence and ran up to the mound, mad enough to bite horseshoes.

There Young Whitelaw was bellowing and swinging his hands in a speech about the Democrats and the Whigs.

"Hey there, ye cockle-brained cuckoo, Young White-law," shouted Farmer Jackson hoarsely. "Stop yer bellowin'! Stop yer blatherin' whoa'in' and yea'in' an' nay'in' like a crazy oaf, I tell ye. Stop it or I'll stuff yer mouth with mud."

"I'm not blathering," said Young Whitelaw, much hurt. "I'm practicing a speech by the Whigs against the Democrats."

"Don't give a rotten apple for what kind of a speech it is, but I tell ye, y're disturbin' my ho'ses when I'm tryin' t' plow. Y're keepin' me from work. Stop that danged yea'in an' nay'in' an' woo'in'. Every time ye woo the Democrats my horses whoa when I want 'em t' giddup. An' every time y' say yea to the Whigs, my ho'ses gee when I want 'em to haw. Stop the bellowin'. If ye don't, I'll drive it out o' ye with a good willow switch."

The boy went off hurt and angry, mumbling to himself, "Some day you'll be glad to listen to me."

Young Whitelaw was right. He kept on practicing his pieces and, as life went along, made as fine speeches as any man and wrote better pieces than many a man. Farmer Jackson stayed Farmer Jackson, but Young Whitelaw became editor of one of the finest newspapers in the land and minister of foreign lands.

That is the kind of story they tell of Whitelaw Reid around Xenia in Ohio.

The Witch of Ohio

I'M going to tell you the story of the only witch trial
that happened in Ohio, from Toledo on Lake Erie to
lovely Gallipolis.

Though many settlers in the Buckeye State came from
New England where there were more witch trials than
should ever 've been, these pioneers lost the foolish be-
liefs when they reached the new broad lands. The air in
the rich valleys of Ohio cleared their minds of silly su-
perstitions, and when they saw the fields and meadows
around the Scioto River they laughed at those black cob-
webs like a strong anvil at a broken hammer.

Now, amongst the early settlers was an old woman
named Abigail Church. She was a good soul and worked
hard, as did most of the pioneer women in those days.
She helped dig the ground, plant, and harvest. She
cooked, mended, washed, and did all other things a
woman has to do. Besides that she told folks' fortunes—
told what would happen, helped 'em find what they lost,
guided young ones in their love troubles, and straight-

ened out all kinds o' kinks in the community. She did this by talking to folks, looking in their faces, and looking in the playing cards.

Many came to her from near and far, came to her little cabin whenever they had some trouble with love, animals, crops, or anything else. And she always asked for twenty-five cents after telling what folks came to learn.

One day Jesse Denton, a riverman, came and said he had lost a pocketbook with money in it. He had searched everywhere and couldn't find it.

Abigail looked at Jesse, asked him many questions—where he had been and whom he had seen; then she shuffled her cards and spoke some words he could not understand. When she was finished, she told him a dark man 'd come and return his pocketbook. He gave her twenty-five cents and went his way.

It didn't take long before a Negro came, said he had found a lost pocketbook, and gave it back to Jesse.

Soon after, young George Badgley came to see Abigail Church and told her of his love troubles. Abigail listened, looked in George's face, spoke some words, looked in the cards, and then told him to go home and all would turn out well in the end. George paid his twenty-five cents and went off satisfied.

Now, you know, even the finest dog has fleas, and there are envious folks everywhere. Each land has its share of 'em plenty. That kind, seeing Abigail Church earning twenty-five cents now and then, reported her to the law and brought her before the judge—as a witch. That was a mighty serious accusation, punishable with half a year in jail and a fine of five hundred American dollars.

Abigail had to get a lawyer to defend her, and she chose young Richard Douglas who had come from New England and settled in Chillicothe. It was Richard Vinton, also from New England, who was her accuser for the State.

The great day came, and there was a big crowd to listen to the first witch trial in Ohio. Twelve men chosen for a jury sat with hands on their knees; Abigail, with bright eyes, was smiling to her friends; young Vinton stood ready to tell what a black witch she was; young Douglas was there ready to defend her; and the judge watched so that justice would be done.

Mister Vinton began by telling that Abigail was working against the laws of the Lord, claiming she could see in playing cards what the Lord had hidden from us in his wisdom. That was witchcraft. She had disobeyed the law of the land by charging twenty-five cents for telling these lies and blasphemies. She was a dangerous woman, for she set peaceful neighbors quarreling and she cheated and defrauded. He used many words telling that and asked the twelve jurymen to find her guilty of these crimes.

Next, young Douglas defended Abigail. He called many witnesses who said that she was a hard-working old woman whose husband had fought fearlessly in the

Revolutionary War. He told that all who went to her
for help were satisfied and content. To prove this he
called George Badgley as a witness. George spoke up
and said that all Mister Douglas had said was true. He
had gone to Abigail for advice and she had given it to
him most satisfactorily. He had paid her twenty-five
cents and was glad to do so.

Then Mister Douglas called the boatman for whom
Abigail had helped find the pocketbook. He spoke no
different from George. In the end General Holcomb of
Chillicothe was called in Abigail's defense and told the
same story the other witnesses had. And he said he had
heard of many men and women who had gone to Abigail for advice and had nothing but praise for her.

After that, Douglas told Abigail to speak for herself,
and she was the kind who could out-twitter any swallow.

"Lands sakes alive!" said she. "Can't tell ef I kin tell
fortunes or not, an' I'm no witch, sure as there's a Lord
in heaven. Ef folks believe I kin tell 'em what to do an'
have a hankerin' to hear 'bout it, it must be so. Don't ye
think so? I got t' earn a livin' an' must be paid for my
time. Recken twenty-five cents for listenin' days long to
their troubles ain't too much. But I kin tell ye, I never
took no money from children or old fools. Never."

After that young Douglas made a long speech against
a silly law that 'd hail a woman to court because some
folks believed in what she told 'em. He said all this in
fine, grand words, and in the end he begged the jurymen
to let Abigail go free.

The judge had listened closely all along, sometimes hiding a smile behind his hand, and now he told the twelve jurymen they'd have to decide whether Abigail was guilty or not.

The twelve jurymen went out but did not stay long. They came back smiling and said Abigail was no witch and could go free.

And so the first and only witch trial in Ohio had a happy ending, as in a fairy tale. The whole town rejoiced. Folks then said:

> What was bitter on Monday,
> Was sweet to remember on Tuesday.

SOUTH BEND

FORT WAYNE

INDIANA

INDIANAPOLIS

TERRE HAUTE

EVANSVILLE

Abe Lincoln in Indiana

Abraham Lincoln
his hand and pen.
he will be good but
god knows When.

This is what Abe Lincoln wrote when he was a boy.

There are a thousand stories about Abe Lincoln, maybe even more, and they are full of juicy kindness and laughter. For Abe Lincoln was a true American with love for folk no matter what their color or degree.

I'll tell you one of these stories. It happened when Abe was a stripling, with plenty of mischief in him like any other young one.

It's a tale that'll bring warm laughter to any boy or girl from eight to eighty or thereabouts.

When Abe was young, he was long an' slab-sided— kind o' gangly in his linsey-woolsey clothes. Big 's a full-grown man, he was stronger than any boy his age living in Little Pigeon Creek in Indiana, and he loved playing pranks that brought warm laughter. He was a good boy,

75

always helping his father and mother. Sarah Bush Lincoln was his second mother, yet she loved him as if he were her own flesh and blood, and Abe loved her just the same.

One time the Lincoln cabin needed painting. The walls were covered with greasy smoke and smudge, black spots from flies, and red spots where mosquitoes had been squashed. Everybody took a hand painting the walls and ceiling, but Abe did most of the work, and as he worked he hummed little riddles like:

> Niddy, niddy, noddy,
> Two heads and a body.

"What yer singin', Abe?" the mother asked.

"It's a riddle, Mother Sairy. Give ye three guesses t' guess it."

Sarah thought for a spell, then she said: "Cain't guess."

"Mother Sairy, it's easy. It is a rollin' pin," and both laughed. Then he hummed:

> Patch on a patch an' a hole in the middle.
> Guess the riddle an' I'll give ye a fiddle.

"Kin ye guess that one?"

"No, I cain't."

"It's the chimney right over the fireplace." Then he pointed to it. Next Abe hummed:

> If a body meets a body in a field o' beans,
> Can a body tell a body what a body means?

They both laughed, and mother and son were mighty pleased. When the work was done the mother said: "Abe, y're the best painter in all Indiany." That made young Abe's ears tingle, and he smiled all over.

"Be mighty keerful, son, an' don't put yer hands on the walls when ye come from the barn or field so 's t' keep it clean for a long time t' come. An' don't kill no skeeters on the walls either, an' be mighty keerful when ye walk so 's ye don't rub yer mop o' hair full o' dirt from the barn on the clean white ceilin'."

He needed that last warning, for I told you Abe was tall's any and then some taller, so that his head touched the ceiling when he was standing up. Everything about him was big, even his nose, and he was forever rubbing and hitting things.

Abe laughed at his mother's speech, solemnly promised to obey, and at the same time was thinking how to play some trick about it.

One sunny afternoon his mother went a-visiting a neighbor, and Abe saw his chance to do what he had in mind.

Two boys his own age, but much smaller, were playing at the horse trough by the barn. He went to 'em and said: "Ye two kin help me in a little game that'll make my mother laugh."

All the countryside knew Abe Lincoln for a prankster, but most of all the boys his own age. They were always pretty pleased to join in the fun.

"Yer feet are full o' mud, and that's just what I need.

Come with me," and he went to the cabin, the others following. "I'll let ye walk on the ceiling."

When they came to the door he picked up one of 'em, carried him into the cabin, and then turned him upside down, head down and feet up. Then, holding him with his strong hands, he made him walk with his feet full o' dirt on the nice white ceiling so that it looked as if someone had walked on it, head down.

Next Abe took the other boy, upended him, and walked him on the ceiling the opposite way. The three looked at the black footmarks on the white ceiling and laughed loud and long, they looked so funny.

The two boys went off, and Abe sat down near the fireplace, a book he had borrowed in his hands, looking as innocent as a pigeon sitting on a perch.

Soon Sarah came back, a small crock o' butter in her arms. She saw the ceilin' and stopped short in her tracks. She looked and she looked, and there was a mighty puzzled look in her face.

"Good earth an' seas!" was all she could say. Then she looked at young Abe sitting at the fireplace and watching her from the corner of his eye.

Sarah was pretty smart. Said she in a stern-like voice: "Abe," she said, "how come ye dirtied that ceilin' with yer footmarks?"

"Better than dirtyin' it with my hair mop."

"Did ye walk on that ceilin'?" she said, trying hard to hold back the laughter that was wanting to come out.

"Guess I did," he said. "Got tired walkin' on the dirt below."

Then the good mother couldn't hold back her laughter any more, and when it let off for a minute she said with tears in her eyes: "Ef ye weren't that big an' I didn't love ye so much I'd turn ye round an' spank ye red."

Abe joined in the laughter, then he told her how the footmarks got on the ceiling.

In that way the stepmother and son came closer in their love for each other, for there's nothin' helps more to greater love than good laughter.

Abe painted the ceiling white all over again to please his mother and to make it look nice.

So Abe Lincoln spent his early days, working, laughing, and bringing joy and good humor everywhere.

Old Man Edmonds and the Ninety-nine Pigs

THERE lived a man in Indiana, in the Hoosier State, who was funnier than a squirrel cracking nuts and who could spin yarns better than a spider spinning webs. They called him Old Man Edmonds, and he told tales taller than a hickory and broader than the Ohio is long. Folks laughed at his roaring whoppers and asked for more, for a good laugh is as heart-warming as sunshine in winter.

Spring had come, when the earth and those on it thawed out and breathed deep the fresh wind and air. Old Man Edmonds came down from his cabin to the village livery stable, where the finest chin-churners were sitting around speaking of this and that.

He was a little fellow with long hair and a long beard. His back was bent and he limped on one leg.

"How'd ye winter up yer way?" the men asked Old Man Edmonds.

"Mighty fine, mighty fine. Finest winter ever had; feelin' fine as my hundred hogs."

"A hundred hogs!" . . . "When did ye ever have a hundred hogs?" . . . "Y' couldn't house 'em if ye had 'em." . . . "Y' ain't got a pen big 'nuf fer a hundred hogs," came from all around.

"Didn't need no pen. Kept 'em in a holler log. Them were mighty smart pigs."

"Ed, guess y' had a mighty jorum o' peach 'n honey."

"Maybe I did an' maybe I didn't, but jest the same I got the finest hundred pigs in Johnson County."

"Where 'd ye keep 'em from freezin' all winter?"

"Doggone, told ye I wintered 'em in a hundred-foot holler log. Maybe 'twas a little longer."

"Where 'd ye git the holler log?"

"Waal, it's a long tale. I'd been noticin' my cattle gettin' thinner 'n thinner though I fed 'em plenty corn. Guessed someone was stealin' my corn, so one night I set watchin' fer the thief. Pretty soon come a flock o' wild turkeys swoopin' down the barn gobblin' corn faster 'n beatin' the devil aroun' a tree. It raised my dander big 'nuf t' catch fire. I rushed at 'em an' grabbed 'em by the legs. Up they swooped, with me hangin' on. Hadn't counted on that an' was figurin' jest what t' do when a hurricane come along, tore me down, an' I felt plumb scared t' death. Fell down right into a holler tree. That's why I've been limpin' all them years.

"Ef ye don't know what's a holler tree I'll tell ye. It is a tree that's all bark and no wood, jest holler all inside.

"Waal, 'twas black 's Egypt in there, only a bit o' moon yon high. So I began climbin' up to git out. Jest got a little way up when that bit o' moon was darkened, an' what d' ye think it was?"

"What?"

"A b'ar. A black b'ar climbin' plumb down over me. Scared me white, fer I'd sure git choked 'n maybe crushed by that b'ar in that holler tree. Jest then I remembered I had a good sharp shuckin' peg in my pocket. Took it out quick an' held it up high. Mister B'ar were comin' down quick, an' soon I grabbed 'm by the tail with one hand an' with the other stuck 'm hard with that shuckin' peg. That made Mister B'ar go up quicker 'n he come down, pullin' me up with 'm.

"When I got out, I leaped on the ground an' ran home an' didn't stop till I got in bed."

"What's that got ter do with yer hundred pigs?"

"Lots. Y' see, the next mornin' I got t' thinkin' an' figurin' 'bout that holler log. Thought t' meself it might come in handy. So I dragged it right t' my barn an' set it 'longside the pigpen. An' didn't it come in handy!

"Mirandy, my sow, jest had a litter o' ninety-nine pigglins. The pigglins crawled right in that holler log, jest in an' out, in an' out, fer fun.

"Come winter, there weren't no room in the pigpen, so they kept on goin' in the holler log fer shelter. But there weren't no room fer all of 'em. So those stayin' out were forever pushin', tryin' t' git in. They'd push so hard to git in, the front ones 'd be pushed out. Then them front ones 'd run quick aroun' the log, git back, an' begin pushin' in.

"All day long an' all night some 'd be inside while some 'd be runnin' aroun' tryin' t' git in an' some 'd be pushin' t' git futher. That kept 'em all good 'n warm all winter long, an' they grew t' be fine, healthy hogs.

"That's how come I'm ready t' take 'em t' market. I come t' town t' git some things I need."

Then Old Man Edmonds walked away limping, his beard flying and his old hat stuck fast on his head. The men around the stable laughed, glad to have so fine a tale-teller as Old Man Edmonds in their state.

The Little Prairie Hen
and the Big Indiana

IN the early days, the people of Indiana built a grand canal in Wabash County to make living easier for the settlers. When the "big ditch" was done, the important citizens of Wabash town wanted the famous Captain "Hail Columbia" and his fine boat, the *Indiana*, known far and wide along the rivers of the Hoosier State, to be the first to come into their town. Thus honor would come to the town, the Captain, and the boat.

There were to be speechmaking, flags and fireworks, and a grand prize of fifty dollars for the captain of the first boat to enter Wabash. That was a great deal of money in those good days. Everyone wanted the famous Captain to win the honors and the prize.

Captain Hail Columbia agreed with the good citizens. He set out from Fort Wayne, Indiana, with a full boat to gain fame and fifty dollars. He stopped at Flint, took on more folks, and continued on the way. Everybody was having a grand time, while the Captain was prepar-

84

ing an eagle-soaring speech for the roaring welcome awaiting him in Wabash town.

To be sure, many another captain and crew dreamed of gaining this fame and fortune—from the little *Prairie Hen*, the smallest boat on the Maumee River, to the *Wabash*, the largest one known in all the state. But folks knew it was only a dream—the *Indiana* would come first into Wabash and cover herself with glory. Just a few felt otherwise, amongst them Captain Patchen of the *Prairie Hen*, that was coming along the canal far behind the *Indiana*.

Night came and the stars high up in the sky beamed on the *Indiana* and the happy crowd. Captain Hail Columbia was jesting red, white, and blue with his friends, and so they came to Lagro, which was only six miles from Wabash.

"Why not stop for the night?" some said. "Folks are now asleep, and such a grand celebration 'll shine best in sunlight. Why not lay off here and come in in the mornin', when everyone is wide awake?"

Captain Hail Columbia agreed. He had friends at Lagro with whom it would be nice to spend the hours. So the boat tied up, and Captain and passengers went off gaily a-visiting. Soon all was still on the water of the canal but for the singing frogs and the chirping insects that filled the grass and bushes.

Afar off, Captain Patchen and the little *Prairie Hen*, drawn by good strong horses, moved along the towpath at a steady pace. The boat was full of Indians, but all were silent, for the night was far gone and everyone was at rest. In good time the little boat came near Lagro, and Captain Patchen, wide awake, noted the *Indiana* tied along the wharf and a great silence over all. He stopped his boat, sent a boy to investigate, and got the news that it *was* the *Indiana*—tied up for the night and not a soul on it! Captain Patchen's heart leaped high as the stars. Jerusalem Cricket! Here was a chance sent by the Lord on high.

"Cap'n Columbia is a mighty smart man," he said, "but this time I'll outsmart 'm."

Standing in the stern, bent forward looking hard in all directions, he ordered the horse boy driving the horses that pulled the boat to go slowly and carefully. Then he and his crew raised the drawing rope high, took planks, and pushed the *Indiana* to the shore. This gave them plenty of room to pass without noise or bumping. Once clear, Captain Patchen ordered the horses to hit it up. Soon they were going over three miles an hour, and in no time the little boat and Captain Patchen were out of sight.

The night moved quick and so did the boat, and when the stars became pale in the sky the *Prairie Hen* was tied up on the wharf of Wabash.

I'll bet you can guess what the folks in Wabash thought when they came in the morning for the celebration and found the *Prairie Hen* with proud Captain Patchen the first there.

Just when the time for the talkfest began and the

money was ready to be given, the *Indiana* and Captain Hail Columbia pulled in. You can just picture their surprise. But Captain Hail Columbia, who was a good fellow, joined in the merrymaking.

There was a grand dinner at the Treaty Ground and a big ball at night in the only brick house in Wabash town.

For the rest of his life, Captain Hail Columbia remembered the good lesson he'd been taught: and that was to keep wide awake while hunting for fame and fortune.

They still tell that tale in Wabash County, and a good tale it is.

Georgie Goes A-Sparkin'

IN the days when Hoosiers grew as big as giants, Georgie Boon was bigger than the biggest and stronger than the strongest. He stood seven feet without his shoes, and he was still growing. Biggest of all were his feet. Maybe they were the biggest in Indiana.

One fall Sunday, when sun and wind made music in the golden red leaves, Georgie Boon thought he'd go a-sparkin'.

He got out his new butternut-brown suit bought in the store only six months before. But when he tried to put it on, it didn't seem to fit too good. Georgie grew that fast. Now those clothes were tight on him as an eelskin stretched on a hoop pole, but after working and sweating he got into 'em. That was enough, he thought. No need for shoes—the air was still warm and the ground soft.

So, going through woods and meadows, through brooks and creeks, he came to the cabin where pretty

Sally lived with her father and mother. Sally was pretty as a daisy and full of fun and frolic.

She said "Howdy" with a laugh and a blush. Sally's parents were friendly, too, and Georgie Boon felt things were going his way. He wished 'em all good evening over and over again.

"Y're right welcome," Sally's mother said.

Then they spoke of the weather and the crops, of hunting and church. But Georgie spoke least of all. He was sitting, filling his eyes and heart with Sally's pink cheeks and Sally's blue eyes and Sally's laughing and giggling.

Suppertime came, and Sally's mother brought mush, and milk and homemade bread. She dished out big bowlsful of mush, handing one to each. When it came to Georgie, he put his big hand across the table for the bowl, his eyes on Sally's face. Not watching, he hit the pitcher and spilled all the milk on the table.

Sally began laughing and kept on and on till the tears ran down her pink, round cheeks. She couldn't stop laughing, so she jumped up and ran out, leaving Georgie with her father and mother.

Georgie got red as a beet and wished the earth 'd swallow him whole. But Sally's mother said, "Guess I kin clean up. Worse happenin's 'n that 've come t' pass."

They began eating, but there was little talking. Georgie was thinking only of Sally, wishing she'd come in, and Sally's parents didn't see much use in talking when they were busy eating.

In the end, Sally's mother cleaned the table and Sally's father filled his pipe with tobacco.

The stars were in the sky in great company and the insects were making a to-do, but there was little talk amongst the three sitting in the cabin.

The Yankee clock kept on going round and round. It was pointing late and time for bed. But Georgie never made a move to go. He was hoping Sally'd come back, but Sally didn't come back.

Sally's father got up. "Time t' go t' bed," he said.

Georgie sat there as if nailed to the wooden bench.

Both parents went to the other side of the cabin, but Georgie, he sat.

A spell of time went by, then Georgie heard Sally's mother say, "Mister George, would ye like to wash yer feet an' stay fer the night?"

A psalm sung by angels wouldn't have been sweeter to Georgie than those words.

"Yes, ma'am!" he cried, for now he was sure to see Sally again.

"I'll bring a pot o' hot water so ye kin wash yer feet," the mother said.

She brought it in, set it near Georgie, and went out.

The pot wasn't too big and Georgie had the biggest feet in Indiana. He worked hard to get his big feet into the little pot, and after a time he got 'em in sideways.

The water was right warm, and the bugs and birds were making the right kind of music outside, and Georgie thought how nice it would be to live with Sally.

But soon he stopped thinking, for his feet were aching mighty strong. He wriggled his toes and wriggled his feet trying to get 'em out, but they just wouldn't come.

There was coughing on the other side of the cabin and Sally's mother said, "Ain't ye done, Mister George?"

Georgie cried, " 'Deed I'm done," and tried harder than ever to get his feet out from the pot. But the feet had swelled in the warm water, and, try as he would, they wouldn't come out. He was getting hot all over, and big drops of sweat ran from his forehead.

There was Sally's mother again: "Mister George, ain't ye done yet?"

"Gee whilliky, ma'am, no. How much did that pot cost?"

"Guess a dollar. Got it from a peddler from up north not long ago."

"One dollar?" Georgie mumbled. "Could be worse." Not far from him stood an ax. He reached out for it and soon that pot was broken in more than one place. Georgie, he never knew before in his life what joy it was to have free feet. He jumped up quick, put a green dollar bill on the table, and ran out without even saying good night.

And so Georgie never married Sally, but he became a fine senator in Washington instead.

Gentlin' the Ram

DID you ever hear the tale of the stubborn ram told around Lake County in Indiana? The tale of the stubborn ram and Sam Woods, green from England and fresh with ideas that made him a fine American and even a lawmaker. If you haven't, here it is, fresh and lusty, told by his own son Sam, even as sons of other early settlers tell it.

Sam Woods came to America to earn an honest living, to think as he pleased, and to build him a home and hearth.

Life in the new land was hard, and young Woods knew little about pioneering ways. But the good Lord who takes care of the sparrow watched over young Woods, and soon he found him a wife from Pennsylvania who knew the work and ways this side o' the ocean.

She helped him build a log house, helped him work the land and clear the fields, and soon they had a home as good as any.

92

As the sun and the moon turned the months, young Woods and his wife worked and prospered. Soon they had horses and cows and oxen and a fine flock of sheep that gave them plenty of wool.

Now, amongst that flock there was a ram that was vicious as a wolf. He was ever contrary and ever looking for trouble.

He didn't like the sheep and he didn't like the cows. He didn't like the horses and he didn't like the birds, and what he liked least of all was the female folk. He just couldn't stand any creature that didn't wear britches. No sooner would he see a skirt than he'd fly into a rage and begin bucking and kicking to beat Jerusalem.

For a long time Sam Woods tried all he knew to teach that ram to be a reasonable creature, for he liked animals. He fed him better than the others, gave him maple sugar, and petted him and spoke kindly to him, figuring sweetness and kindness would sweeten that cantankerous beast. But it was no use. No sooner would that ram see the sight of a skirt or petticoat than he'd fly into a rage as if he had the seven-year's itch.

The women from near and far, and, most of all, Mistress Woods said Sam didn't know how to treat the beast and he'd never get anywhere with bribery. The best way would be to use a good hickory stick or starve him into being good.

For a long time there were great arguments between husband and wife.

Wife said: "Get rid o' that beast."

Husband said: "I'll make that bearded wildcat act like any other animal."

Wife said: "Then why don't you?"

Husband said: "I will, in good time."

Wife said: "It's takin' a mighty long time."

Husband said: "It's a poor wife that don't know the virtue of patience."

Wife said: "Patience has no endin'."

The arguments had no ending, either.

But one day Sam said he had had enough. "I'm through bribing that beast, he just won't listen to reason. I want peace in the house and peace in the field, and I am ready to teach that ram a lesson."

The next morning he put on his wife's oldest red flannel petticoat and a shawl around his shoulders and over his head, so that you'd swear he was a woman. Then, taking a strong hickory stick, he walked into the pasture where the sheep and the buck were grazing.

Mistress Woods stood at the gate to watch the game.

No sooner did the ram lay eyes on his master than he thought it was a woman, and, lowering his head, he went at him full blast as if he had the devil in his hoofs. But Master Woods was ready. He raised his stick and began belaboring that unreasonable beast that attacked womenfolk who never did him any harm.

But this was a ram of rams. He didn't seem to mind the rain of blows at all. He bore in on his master and attacked him fiercely. Soon the master had to retreat toward the house.

Mistress Woods, who had been at the gate watching, was not only a good worker but a mighty smart woman as well, and a quick-thinking one.

"Lead that beast to the root cellar!" she screamed. "Just lead him to the root cellar door! Lead him right to the door. The cellar is all empty!"

Then she ran to the root cellar and opened the wooden door, standing close behind it.

Sam understood and did the very thing. He led the ram right to the door of the root cellar, and when the animal was close to it he jumped to the side, threw his full weight against it—and the creature was safely in. Mistress Woods shut the door and put the heavy wooden bolt into the slot.

"Now, husband," she cried triumphantly, "I'll finish what you so well began. If the good stick didn't work, maybe an empty stomach'll do the trick."

"Well, let's try it," said Master Woods, wiping the perspiration from his face. "If it doesn't work there'll be one ram less in the world."

That day and the next day the ram didn't get a blade of grass or a drop of water.

The morning of the third day Mistress Woods took a handful of grass and a pot of water. Her husband followed. "Now, you, Sam, open the door just a wee bit, just a least bit for that beast to see it's a woman in a petticoat that feeds 'm and gives 'm water."

Sam opened the door, just enough to put a hand in. The animal made a wild dash at the door, but when he smelled and saw the grass, he stopped and began eating. Then Mistress Woods gave him a little water.

This she did two and three times a day for a few days until she came right into the cellar with an apronful of grass and a bucket of water in her hand.

The ram began to learn that it was a woman in a petticoat that fed him when he was hungry and gave him drink when he was thirsty. He ate and drank and sure did not attack her. And soon that ram was as gentle as a lamb.

"You see, husband," Mistress Woods 'd say, "bribery's never got a man anything 'cept trouble." And Mistress Woods spoke true.

The Hat in the Moon

YOU have heard many, many tales of the man in the moon, but folk in Indiana say there is no man in the moon at all. What you think is a man is really a good simple old Quaker hat, such as was worn by Quakers in the olden days, and this is how it came into the moon.

There lived not far from Richmond, in the Hoosier State, Ebenezer and Charity, two fine Quakers as ever there were.

Ebenezer was a good man, worked hard on his land, and, with the help of the Lord, he prospered. Charity, his good wife, worked hard in the home and helped much to add to the prosperity of the two.

They were God-fearing folk and went to meeting, as they call their hours of worship, every Sunday, thanking the Lord deep in their hearts for health and home and all the good things of the world they owned.

As time went its way, the number of good things of the world they had grew. They had fine horses and fine wagons and even a fine buggy with which to ride to meetin' and to friends.

97

Now, every year there was one grand meeting in Richmond, which was a good-sized town in Wayne County. Good Quakers and their wives and children came from farms and villages to meditate and pray, to see their friends and neighbors, and to buy things they were in need of. So did Ebenezer and Charity, in their shiny new buggy with a pair of fine horses and in their best simple clothes.

In Richmond they met friends and fellow Quakers, and they walked up and down the streets to talk and look at the goods the merchants of the town were showing.

They saw many things and, amongst them, a place full of fine beaver hats—large, high, round, smooth, and velvety—much more beautiful than the simple felt hats the Quakers of Indiana wore. Ebenezer looked at those beaver hats and felt a longing in his heart for one of them. It sure would look fine on him, and Ebenezer loved fine things, though the Quaker creed spoke only of simple things.

Try as he would, he could not get that dark-brown beaver hat out of his mind, nor the hankering for it. He saw it shining wherever he went. He saw it on his head and saw how it made of him a more important man. The next time he was alone that day, though he knew it was against the Quaker creed, he went to the store, bought the hat, and put it safe under the buggy seat.

The meeting done, the friends seen, the news gathered, the things bought, Ebenezer and his wife set out for home. The way was long, but the horses were strong, so they kept on jogging along between the green fields and the turning trees, speaking of the things that had happened while they were in Richmond. Soon a large, full moon, silvery and soft, came into the sky and followed them pleasantly along the way.

They passed by a quiet little pond, and, looking into it, Ebenezer saw himself with his hat on his head and then he remembered the fine brown beaver he had bought. He took the one he wore and set it down before his feet, pulled out the new one from under the seat, put it on his head, and turned proudly to his wife.

Now, Charity, sitting quietly in her gray Quaker bonnet, was a fine upright body and a simple one. At the sight her eyes opened wide. Never before had she seen her husband decked out in such finery, a thing Quakers frowned upon. For a second she was speechless—and then her breath came back. She let out a wild shriek that went through the night like frightened thunder. She shrieked because she didn't think it fit for a Quaker man to wear such worldly finery, and she shrieked because of something else she saw . . . and which Ebenezer didn't see. Then her hand went up high, first pointing to his head and then to the silvery moon.

Ebenezer looked up, and there he saw . . . a sight that took his breath away and put fear in his heart!

The moon was no longer clear and silvery as it had been when they had set out.

Now there was a cloudiness in it, a round cloudiness,

grayish brown . . . no, it was no cloudiness, but a shadow of the Quaker hat Ebenezer had spurned.

"That's your warnin' an' your punishment fer your worldliness," cried Charity. "I saw it flyin' up."

Ebenezer never said a word, but sat still, staring at the moon and the Quaker hat in it.

He took off that fancy beaver hat and never put it on again. He bought another simple brown felt Quaker hat which he wore for the rest of his life. Though Ebenezer repented in his heart and never repeated his foolishness, that Quaker hat has stayed up in the moon ever since as a reminder to all who look longingly at worldly goods for which they have no need.

And when you come to Indiana and travel on a warm evening in the full moon with some Hoosier folk through Wayne County, or even Randolph, Delaware, Henry, Shelby, Fayette, and other counties, you'll hear the tale of the Quaker hat in the moon, even as I heard it.

The Colonel's Blanket

IN THE circuit-riding days, four men were a-journeying down Danville to the court meeting. One was Judge Wicks, one was Hiram Brown, a smart young lawyer, one was Calvin Fletcher, a preacher, and the fourth was an argufying colonel.

The sun was shining, the wind was blowing, the brown leaves were falling, and the four, like good Hoosiers, whiled away the time talking. But the one who did the most chin churning was the colonel, properly named William Quarles.

He was bragging to beat dragoons. He was a mighty hunter, he wasn't scared of man or beast, and he could battle storms and swim rivers.

"There's no man can hunt bear or coon or deer or anything as I can. I've gotten 'em in fair weather and in stormy jest as well."

So it kept on till the others were sick and tired of listening to 'm. The sun had run behind the clouds like it was tired hearing the boasting and the bragging, and a sharp wind was blowing hog bristles through men and beasts.

"Guess rain 's on the way—maybe a storm," said the Judge.

"Don't tell me you're scared of a little wind, Judge," cried bragging Will. "Don't look to me like rain. I've been through hurricanes that rooted giant trees from virgin land. This is a spring zephyr, Judge," and Quarles laughed loud. "Fact is, I like a good stormy wind."

They kept on riding while the wind was growing fiercer and the sky was getting darker. They were still a long ways from Danville.

"If you like good wind come from the Lord," said young Fletcher, "you'll get your fill of it. I, too, like riding in a mighty wind."

Now and then big drops were coming through the trees under which the four horses were trotting fast. There was a cabin on the road.

"Might stay here for the night," the Judge said.

"I'm for goin' on," said Hiram Brown, the lawyer.

"An' I'm for the same," said Preacher Fletcher.

"Well, maybe the Judge is right and we ought to stay. It's getting dark," said Colonel Quarles, a worried look on his face.

"You aren't scared, good friend?" said Hiram Brown.

"Scared! Not me!" cried Quarles. "But Judge Wick is a knowing man, and if he wants to stay, then I'm with 'm."

"Leave Judge Wick follow his own mind. I'm for going on, and if you're not scared you'll come along," said Brown.

Judge Wick didn't say a word, and so Quarles was silent, too. He followed with no end of anger boiling in him, for it was really he that wanted to stop. He was tired, but he wouldn't let on.

Young Fletcher was ahead, with Brown behind and the others close up. They couldn't go fast, for the path was narrow, and it was pretty dark.

The wind howled in the branches and rain was now falling thick, wetting men and beasts and making Quarles angrier all the time.

Now he sang a different tune. Instead of boasting, he was cursing. But the wind roared so loud you couldn't hear a word.

Suddenly Hiram, who was in front, cried out, "We're off the path."

"Guess we lost our way," said Fletcher.

"That's unfortunate," said the Judge.

"And whose smart idea was it? Who is to blame, I'd like to know," cried Quarles. "Now we'll all suffer for your pigheadedness, Squire Brown."

"Drown your squawking," cried Hiram, "and let's look for shelter for the night."

They kept going this way and that way, following Hiram till he stopped in an open spot overhung by branches of beech and hickory.

"Here the rain don't come so quick," he said. "No use going farther, we'll not find anything better."

"I hope Indians aren't 'round," said the colonel.

"Bet if they were," said Hiram, "you'd be the first to be scalped—you've got the thickest mop." Hiram was dismounting, and they tied the horses to the trees. Then they unloaded the animals and tried to make a fire. But for all the trying it was no use, so they sat down on the wet leaves to eat whatever each one had.

The first to finish was Squire Brown and, having no blanket, he got up and roamed around to find a dry spot for sleeping. Suddenly his foot stumbled against a bundle. He felt it and knew it was a wool blanket. He picked it up and, without a word to a soul, rolled himself in, settled down, and went to sleep. Soon wind and rain were no more to Hiram Brown than a golden crown to a wet muskrat.

It didn't take long before each one found a dry spot and was rolled in his own blanket.

All except William Quarles. He kept on looking in the dark for his blanket, grumbling all the time. But all the looking was no use. He couldn't find it. In the end, he lost his patience.

"You took my blanket," he cried to young Fletcher.

"I did not," Fletcher said, "I don't take what don't belong to me. You saw me packing one." And he turned the other way.

"Did you take it, Judge?" said Quarles next.

"I'm a judge and not a thief," cried Judge Wick. "You've been raising a ruckus all day, and if you don't **stop** I'll fine you for contempt o' court."

"Then it's Hiram Brown who took it," roared Quarles. "I didn't see him load any blankets on his horse. Nor did anyone else, either. Hey, you, Hiram, return my stolen property!"

But Brown only turned on the other side.

"Get up, you gallows bird!" Quarles bellowed, giving Brown a good shove. "Get up and return my blanket. Get up, I said!"

Brown awoke. For the moment he didn't quite understand what all the ruckus was about. But when he heard Quarles roaring like a bull, "Return my blanket, you horse thief! You stole my blanket!" Hiram said slowly, with sleep still in his eyes and voice, "On just what grounds do you base your evidence, brother?"

"When we started out you said we weren't needing blankets, and I had the wisdom to take one. Mine 's gone and you've got one. It's my blanket. I must've dropped it, and you picked it up."

Now Hiram Brown was fully awake. He raised his voice above the storm and shouted, "Aye, good friend, quite true, I did find a blanket that had no owner. I found it lying lonesome in the howling wilderness and I've no intentions of surrendering it until some good man claims it with a better claim than just saying it's his. I intend to keep it until an owner 'll tell me its color and its partic'lar markings. Whether it's brown or green, and if it has a black spot in the middle. Can you tell me that?"

Well, that just twisted Quarles' disposition altogether

out of shape. It was a new blanket, and he had never examined it for markings. He was so mad he couldn't speak.

The other two, seeing the way the wind was blowing, said that Brown was right and Colonel Quarles would have to give better proof that the blanket was his. That could only be done in full light—the next morning.

You should 've heard Quarles. He called them thieves and liars, he called 'em names I'd be ashamed to tell.

Said Fletcher, who felt a little sorry for Quarles: "Gentlemen, you mustn't quarrel. Perhaps the colonel is telling the truth. Perhaps the blanket does belong to Colonel Quarles, and if that's the case, Squire Brown, you ought to return it."

But Judge Wicks said sternly: "The colonel'll have to wait till the morning, when we can have better light on the subject."

"Suppose I catch a cold in the wind and rain and die!"

"There's a good point, Colonel," said Hiram Brown, wrapped in the blanket. "Self-preservation is the first law of life. I've a wife and children who would suffer if I caught a cold and died, but you, Colonel Quarles, are a bachelor, and so my life is much more important than yours. The whole state of Indiana 'd mourn for me. That's your own argument. Tomorrow morning, if you can prove the blanket is yours, I'll return it to you. Now let me sleep in peace. Remember! All the way, you said you didn't mind wild winds and weather. Now you have a chance to prove it."

Then Hiram Brown went to sleep, and so did the others.

As for Colonel Quarles, he was left with his bragging an' boasting, which sounded grand in words but gave little warmth on a cold and rainy night. And that should teach many a one a lesson.

God's Own Country

INDIANY 'S God's own country, and don't you say a word agin' it. If you do, Indiana folk'll fix a crowbar under Lake Erie and turn that lake over an' flood every town an' city even far as New York. Jest remember that!

That soil in the Hoosier land 's rich. If you stick sumpin' in the ground it'll begin growin' afore you kin wink an eye. An' Lord! how it grows!

One day Eb, down in Adams County, blowed down some turnip seeds. Jest common seeds he got from a relation over in Nashville, Brown County, and he blowed 'em down in the earth in nice furrows, leavin' plenty o' space in between 'em. Then he took punkin seeds, common ones he got from the same relation, an' blowed 'em with his mouth in rows alongside the turnip seeds, leavin' plenty o' space atween for growin'.

When he was finished plantin' the field in this new-fangled way, he turned t' walk to his cabin. He'd gone jest about halfway when he thought he heard a queer heavin' an' pushin' noise. He turned his head an', sugar-

lip wildcats!, them turnip seeds was up out o' the ground
an' growin' fast. Eb, he stood with his mouth open wide
as a woodchuck's hole. An' while he was lookin', those
turnips kept on growin' right along an' changin' color
jest 's turnips do. Then he felt somethin' touchin' his
cowhide boots, curlin' snake-like. He looked down an',
jumpin' Indians!, 'twas a punkin vine from the seeds he
jest planted. They'd grown long 'nuf to reach his boot.
An' now they was growin' an' growin' an' growin' all
the time!

Eb 'd never seen the like before an' got kind o' rab-
bity. The vine was gettin' thicker, curlin' stronger an'
higher round his leg, an' he began runnin', tryin' to reach
the rail fence away from the vine. But the vine was gettin' stronger 'round his legs, an' 'twas only by puttin' all
his strength in his shanks that he got away from it.

B'gosh! Now more vines had come up, runnin' up the
fence too.

Eb was a quick-thinkin' man, so he pulled out his Barlow knife an' began slashin' right 'n left, cuttin' through
them vines. He was doin' mighty well, for he was a
strong Hoosier man, but now there was sumpin' else.
The punkins from them vines was growin' fast, too.
They were growin' so fast, two of 'em 'd gotten long
'nuf t' reach the fence closin' in on Eb. He began slashin'
at 'em.

I told ye Indiany 's God's own up-snortin' land, and
when things come there, they come thick.

The turnips an' punkins Eb planted were growin' fast

as fire. They was comin' right up to the fence, an' Eb thought he'd better git help.

He shouted loud enough t' be heard in the next county, an' his pappy rushed out t' see what the mouth-shootin' was about.

Seein' his son Eb was in trouble, he ran up, grabbed one o' them turnips, raised it on high, turned it round an' round his haid, an' smashed it smack 'gainst the nearest punkin, knockin' it t' hash. Next, he did the same to the other punkin. After that, he took out his Barlow knife, an' both father an' son slashed through the vines that had grown like a jungle.

When Eb was loose, both hoofed it t' make the grass burn and reached the cabin, where they praised the Lord for settlin' in a land where the earth is so rich.

The next day son an' pappy went out harvestin' an', bein' two o' them turnips made a bushel, they sold near eleven hundred bushels o' turnips. Besides, they got rid o' seventy-four wagonloads o' punkins far 's Indianapolis, makin' a good penny with little work save the cartin'.

Now, wouldn't y' call Indiany God's own country?

Why the Devil Keeps Out of Indiana

MAYBE ye don't know beans when a bag 's open, but ye'll know quick 's cricket why the Devil keeps away from under the good earth in Wabash County in Indiana when ye are through hearin' this.

There lived in North Manchester in Indiana two fine lumbermen named John and Ben. John was big as an old tree and Ben was big as a barrel, and 'twas said that they both used grindstones for pillows and ate razor soup first thing in the morning. When it came to cussing and using bad words they were even worse than a drove of Ohio boatmen.

They could cuss the bark off a tree. They could cuss the scales off a fish and the feathers off a brass monkey. Now, that wasn't a nice thing, but what could folks of Manchester do? This is a free country. But the Devil, who is always flitting about t' find candidates for his domain way down under, just smiled and watched Ben Barker and John Traverse pretty close.

One spring day, Ben and John bought a fine piece of

timberland, figuring how they'd make a good penny on it. They set to work at once cutting. From sunrise till sunset the chips were flying thick 's snowflakes, but the toad words from their mouths flew thicker. On the fifth day, near sunset, they were cutting a big oak thick as a bear 's long. Both men were pretty much tuckered out.

Spoke John: "Guess we better let the tree fall 'longside the path."

"No, t'other way 's better."

And right then, both fell off the handle into a roarin' argument. The trees shook with anger at the words these two used, and the green leaves, they turned yellow and pale. Every lumberman working near ran, the language was so hot it burned their ears.

The Devil with the green horns, he heard the argument way down in Boston, and he rushed up and rubbed his hands so the sparks flew. He knew for sure he'd get these two.

And the Devil, he guessed right. Soon after, ol' John up 'n died, and the Devil grabbed him quick and took him down below, right under Wabash County, where there was a special place fer Hoosiers that didn't act as they oughter.

Now, ol' John, one day long before he died, after a tough quarrel with his friend Ben, figured out a mean way t' pay him back for it. He went to a lawyer who was so crooked his grave had t' be dug with a corkscrew, and between the two of them they fixed it up so Ben would have to pay a barrel of money to the heirs of John.

When Ben found this out after John's death he near burst with fury. He let loose a waterfall of words the like was never heard in Indiana and then got even madder—so mad that he got sick from it, and soon he, too, up 'n died just the same as ol' John.

When the Devil with his long tail and short horns heard this, he rushed up and whisked Ben down to his own hot home where ol' John was.

Just as you'd guess, the first thing ol' John saw was Ben Barker.

Now, there's three things you can't make over: a stubborn mule, an old miser, an' a swearing lumberman. These two fellows lit into each other like roosters early in the morning. The swearing words, they came faster than greased lightning. Each one tried to talk on both sides o' the road. The Devil with the green horns standing around first laughed, but when those swearing words came faster an' faster, the other devils opened their eyes wide. They had never heard anything like this. The roaring of the cuss words was louder than the roaring of the red fires all around. And it got worse 'n worse all the time. Fact is, it was the worst language ever heard in Wabash County in Indiana on the good earth or under it. Every minute it was getting worse, and in the end the chief Devil couldn't stand it any more. He was getting scared and worried about what would happen to the character of the young devils, hearing such bad language.

He gathered all the young devils around him and told

them t' scat fast and never to come near where those two lumbermen were.

So he left the field to Ben Barker and John Traverse a-cussing each other.

Whether they are still at it right now, way down deep in Wabash County, I can't tell. But what I can tell you is that that is the reason why the Devil never could get a foothold in the good state of Indiana.

The Sad Tale of Tom the Catfish

THERE lived a little fellow in Grant County in Indiana who loved fishing more 'n anything. One day he caught a catfish young as himself and so too little to eat.

It was a mighty pretty catfish glistening in the sun, with fine, long whiskers, so little Obediah put him in a horse trough and fed him every day the same way he fed his dog and his cat and his bird. Soon that little catfish knew Obediah the same as his dog and cat and canary knew him. Fact is, the fish came to know the boy's voice even far away. When he'd be way off, that fish 'd come to the edge, stick out his head, and wait for his master and the hand that fed 'm. After a time, the fish got kind o' used to breathing the air in the outside world even as he did under the water. Soon he got so used to the air, he'd keep his head out o' the water for hours, waiting for his master.

Next thing you know, that fish jumped out of the trough an' began following the boy. Followed him everywhere just like his dog. Followed him even in the

115

house, and slept under the bed just the same as the dog, and ate out o' the same plate, too.

That kept on for a long time till fall came, when the boy had to go to school.

Jedediah honeysuckle! If the dog and Tom—that's what the boy called his catfish—didn't follow the boy right t' the schoolhouse, the dog barking, the fish flopping. When they came to the school, dog and fish, they lay down in the grass while their master blabbed his lesson with the others in the classroom.

Tom the catfish followed Obediah every day t' school for months and months, every blessed day. He flopped pretty near as fast as the dog could run.

Many was the time fish and dog, and maybe the cat, too, 'd play together like a bunch o' rollicking puppies. Reckon that catfish liked it better 'n rollin' around in cold water and getting all wet. By this time he had no use for water at all except for drinking.

One day, it was right around Thanksgiving, and the air was tangy and crisp like a Baldwin apple, Obediah, Rover, the dog, and Tom were romping and jumping through the yellow leaves on the road. It was a sight t' see that catfish going flippidy flop—up and down and all around. Soon Rover and Obediah, they got ahead while Tom was flopping after 'em the best he could. So they came to a creek that had a round log for crossing. Obediah skipped and jumped across it, singing "Yankee Doodle," the dog followed, barking joyfully, and Tom came flopping behind. He had got near over the log when, kerplap!, he flopped sideways and fell into the water.

The water was cold and running fast, and Tom was carried away. Dog and master ran so fast and so far they never noticed it, and Tom, the poor catfish, could not even cry out for help. Y' see, he was so unused to being a fish that the water filled his mouth and eyes. He gurgled and he gasped and came up three times trying to catch a breath of air . . . but it was no use. Tom the poor catfish . . . he drowned!

'Twasn't long afore Obediah and Rover missed Tom and looked for him everywhere. They didn't find him so they figured he'd gone back to his home to the river. 'Deed he had, but not the way they figured.

The Miracle Flame

THERE lived not far from Hindostan in Indiana a pioneer farmer, his wife, and their little child. They were God-loving folk—they labored and they reaped and they were contented, though there were many hardships in the wooded wilderness.

There was ever song and cheer in their home, for Thomas, the father, was a fine fiddler. The day's labor done and the meal eaten, Thomas would play tunes that brought warmth to the heart.

Folk often asked him to play at frolics, raisings, and weddings, and he hardly ever said no.

One time, late in the fall, neighbors wanted him to come to their cabin to fiddle for an evening's frolic after the day's corn shucking.

At first he said no, because his little child was not well.

"You go," said Esther, his wife, "I'll stay here with the babe an' do the work. Don't be late comin' home."

She kept on urging him. "It's a warm evenin'. Ye

118

needn't have no fear 'bout us. Jest go alone this time."

So he went his way, fiddle under his arm and no fear in his mind. Through the woods he went, on paths made by Indians and animals, 'til he reached Hindostan to bring good cheer to the folk of the settlement.

Esther, the good wife who stayed behind, did the work a pioneer woman did in those days. First she put the child to sleep in its little low bed next to hers, singing to it the snatch of a tune she knew her husband 'd play.

> Gone again, what shall I do?
> Gone again, what shall I do?
> Gone again, what shall I do?
> Skip to mah Lou, mah darlin'.

The child liked it and gurgled, so Esther sang another verse, changing it a little to fit her feelings.

> Can't get another one sweeter 'n you.
> Can't get another one sweeter 'n you.
> Can't get another one sweeter 'n you.
> Skip to mah Lou, mah darlin'.

The child's eyes were half closed, so the mother bent down, kissed her, and tucked her in. Then, taking one more look at the babe in the wooden bed, she went out.

First she milked the cow and put the milk in a cool place. The sun had gone from the sky and it was getting dark. She went back into the house, took a good-sized log, put it on the embers, and covered it with ashes to make sure the good fire wouldn't go out. Then she went out again, but not before she had looked at the babe sleeping peacefully. She walked straight to the little wooden shed where they kept their few chickens, to lock them securely against foxes and other animals who might harm them.

A thin sliver of a young moon came into the sky while she was busy with the wooden latch and door to close the shed. Something was holding that door from closing proper. She had it near tight when she heard a noise every settler in those days feared—the long, curdling howling of wolves. The sound seemed right on top of her and sent a chill down her spine.

She turned around and there, not fifty paces back, was a wolf, jaws wide open so you could see the white teeth. Three other animals were right behind him. . . .

Pioneer women had to think quick. There was no time to run into the house where the babe was sleeping. The beasts must be kept away from the child! Better run into the chicken shed and so keep the attention of the wild animals on herself until help came. . . .

She got inside quicker 'n a cat could wink an eye and held the door tight with both her hands.

As is the way of wolves once certain of their prey, they were willing to wait. So they sat down, four of 'em, before the shed, facing the door, howling now and then with jaws wide open. Esther held on to the door inside, praying to the Lord to send help before the wolves would think of going into the house where the babe was peacefully sleeping.

The night grew dark, insects began their night song, but the wolves did not leave the hen shed. And Esther prayed and prayed for a miracle to happen.

Suddenly there was a sound of crying. Her child! She had awakened and was crying for her mother. Esther turned frozen, and her knees gave way under her, for the wolves had stopped their howling! She prayed fiercely to the Lord to save her child.

The babe was crying louder, and the wolves rushed for the cabin. The mother let the door go and stepped out of the shed.

Now the wolves were inside the cabin. It was dark in there. Just the child crying! The wolves were stamping about on the floor! Then something strange happened. Suddenly a fierce flame leaped up, lighting the walls and the bed—the little bed in which the child was sitting up.

A miracle flame blazing high! Like a blaze from heaven!

The stamping of the beasts on the puncheon floor had made the back log on the fireplace roll over, causing it to flare up in a great blaze.

The wolves were frightened by the blinding light and ran out howling. But Esther, the mother, raced to the cabin like a shooting star. She locked the door quickly and sank down on the floor with tears in her eyes and voice, and thanked God for answering her prayer for a miracle in her great moment of need.

And since then they tell the tale around Hindostan in Indiana, how God helped Esther to save her child with a miracle. And a good tale it is, which is why I am telling it to you.

Copperhead in the Bin

THE State of Indiana has every kind of folk, from the smartest in the land to some that aren't smart enough to come in out of the rain.

One fine day, two men were shelling corn in a corn-crib. You guess which kind of folk they were. The crib was near full of corn, and it was kind of dark inside. They were talking and shelling.

Said Lem, who was the taller: "Why did ye make such a ruckus in yer bed last night?"

" 'Cause I'm skeered o' ghosts. I seen 'em comin' with shootin' lanterns."

"Them's lightnin' bugs."

"Some is, an' some ain't. I know."

So they kept on shelling the corn off the dry cobs.

The two were sitting crosswise, comfortable and warm near an upturned barrel. It was homey 'n quiet an' just nice for chewing the fat.

Said Lem: "D'ye know, I once saw a baar. It was a mighty big one an' so I ran, an' when it was gittin' too

123

near fer comfort, I climbed up a cornstalk that was standin' right near. That cornstalk was thick 's a twen'y-year swamp maple. I was goin' higher an' higher. . . ."

Now, the two men were sitting on the puncheon floor, all rotten and full of holes. They were near an upturned barrel that was standing a little on its side. Just as Lem was saying the words "higher an' higher" his hand went near the barrel and . . . out shot a something from under the dark!

You couldn't see exactly what it was, but it was kind o' thick and curved. It shot out sudden-like at Lem's hand and struck his finger again and again and again. It wasn't a deep cut, but kind o' stinging pricks—light an' strong, just like a needle.

"Gosh 'l Mighty!" Lem roared, "it's a copperhead. Did y' see it?" The blood froze in his body and he began shivering like an aspen leaf.

"It sure was a copperhead, and yer goin' t' die," bellowed Jimmie Hoge, jumping up. "Quick, in the cabin. We'll send fer the doctor."

They rushed out of the corncrib past the barn into the house, both roaring, "Copperhead! Copperhead!" Lem held his hand high.

In the cabin Lem fell on the bed. His wife rushed in, and so did his old-maid sister and the children. They all shouted, no one knowing what to do. Two sisters who lived nearby and had come to borrow some salt ran in when they heard the to-do. All were scared cold. The children began crying, and the women advised this and that, for everybody knew that the bite of a copperhead meant sure death.

"Get the corn likker." . . . "Get jalap." . . . "Maybe calomel?" . . . "Boil some blue ash leaves." They cried many more things, while Lem groaned and moaned worse every minute.

Cried Lem's wife: "Dan,"—that was her eldest son— "Dan, saddle the horse and git the doctor."

Dan ran out quick.

Jimmie Hoge brought the likker, and Lem swallowed plenty, till tears came in his eyes and he was coughing and spluttering.

The women, keeping up the tongue-whacking, tied Lem's arm with an apron so the poison wouldn't travel to the rest of his body.

After a time Dan came back with the doctor. The doctor looked at Lem's hand, saw the few red punctures in it, saw it wasn't swollen, and shook his head. "Did y' see the copperhead bitin'?" he said.

"With my own eyes," replied Jim Hoge. "The critter was thick 's an arm an' long 's law."

"Waal," said the doctor, "let's go in the corncrib and get that critter 'afore it bites anyone else." An iron rod stood next to the stove. "Heat that iron rod, Jim, and we'll burn that beast so it can do no harm to any man."

Jim put the rod in the fire till it got red hot. Then, picking it up with a rag, the two went into the corncrib. Inside they walked slowly, Jim's hand outstretched with the hot rod.

They came to the barrel and poked all around and under. Then the rod touched something soft.

There was a wild screeching and fluttering and out flew . . . a hen, making screaming noises the like were never heard in Indiana.

That hen had been setting under the barrel, and maybe she just couldn't stand Lem's tale and stuck her head out and pecked Lem's hand!

Doc Hawks looked at Jim, and Jim looked like a sheep in the rain.

The two went back to the house and told Lem about it, and Lem got up from the bed.

To this day folk all over the Hoosier State tell of the farmer who thought the pecking of a hen was the bite of a copperhead.

Remember well, keep in mind,
An old cow's tail hangs down behind.

Shiny Tales of Vincennes

IN Vincennes, the oldest town in Indiana, most men in bygone days lived truly according to the word of the Lord. There were French folk from Canada and there were Creoles from the South, there were Jews from Germany and there were folk from Ireland and other lands—all fine Americans. They trusted one another and dwelt in friendship with one another.

Now, amongst these folk there was a Jewish merchant, and his name was Adam Gimbel. "Honest Adam," they called him, and there was not a more honest man in all the town of Vincennes. He sold things folk needed, and everybody trusted him. They trusted him so much that whenever some citizen had a little gold or silver money and didn't want to keep it in his house, he took it to Adam's house. There he left it with the good merchant until such time when it would be needed. It was ever safe with Adam.

To him also came the good priest of the town, Bishop Simon Bruté, who went up and down the country begging for gifts for the church and the poor. He always brought the money people gave him to honest Adam to keep until it was needed for a Christian purpose.

He'd open the door and say cheerfully and quietly, "Monsieur Adam, may God bless you and your home. Here is what good people gave me today in the name of God." After that he'd put down a little bag in which he kept the money he had gotten.

"People are good, and the Lord makes them so. The Lord sent you here to help them," Adam would reply. He would smile, take the money, and put it away, adding, "Come back whenever you need it, good father, and you will always find it here."

So it kept on. One evening the priest came in with the money he had gathered for the poor and put his little bag on the counter, as he always did. Adam said to him:

"You bring me whatever you gather, good father, and leave it here for me to keep and never count your money. Aren't you afraid I will take some of it?"

The man of God smiled kindly and replied:

"Friend Adam, I know you for an honest man even as all the townsfolk know you and trust you. I know when I come here to take the money back to give to the poor, I will find more than what I have left with you. Your honesty and kindness to the people of this town are what sunshine and rain are to flowers of God."

Then the two looked at each other, the man who trusted in God and the man whom folk trusted, and there flowed between them a stream of warm understanding and friendship. For Adam had always added his bit to the alms of the poor, he was that kind of man, and the good father knew it.

Such were the folk who were the foundation on which Vincennes in Indiana was built.

Now let me tell you another shiny tale which was told to me by three sisters in Vincennes—Josephine, Martha, and Emma, who live in the ways of the Lord. It is the tale of a miracle the Lord wrought for the people of Vincennes.

That, too, was in the days of Bishop Simon Bruté, the saintly man who came from France to work amongst the folk on the Wabash River. There's no end of tales about him, for he brought the warmth of the sun and the sweetness of the moon to the settlers of Vincennes.

Now, the good bishop was also a doctor and a worker, and there was no task put upon him by the church and by folk that he did not do with joy in his heart and willingness of spirit. Everybody in Vincennes loved him near as much as they did the Lord in heaven.

One fine summer morning, when the corn stood high and fruits and greens grew lush, some folk rushed behind the cathedral, on which the masons were at work, to the little house where the bishop lived.

"Good father," they cried, "come quick to our aid. There are thousands of army worms coming from the hills and prairies to devour the corn we grow to feed us in the winter. Come, help us, for we don't know what to do."

The priest ran with the townsfolk, and soon he saw thousands and thousands of army worms striped black and yellow.

They came in companies and platoons, close to one another, like a giant, wriggling army, marching-crawling in the same direction.

They had cleaned the grass in the prairie, they had devoured the small grain, and now they marched on the town to eat the corn they liked as much as did the folk of Vincennes. Right then they were passing by, south of the river bend, and had begun eating the thick, strong, green juicy stalks, the broad leaves, and green corn husks crowned with pale-yellow tassels waving gaily in the wind.

Once they began eating the corn, it would take little time before there would be no stalk left, only sickly stubbles not fit for man or animal.

"Save us our corn, holy father," the people cried. "Save us our food."

"I can't save your food, good people," the bishop said, "but the Lord on high can, and so we will all pray to Him in our need."

He raised his hands on high and cried:

"Lord Jesus, who feeds all creatures, look down kindly on Thy people and help them in their plight. Save this good crop so these people may live and worship You."

Then a great miracle happened.

The army of worms climbed down from the half-eaten stalks, climbed down slowly on their thick legs, wriggling so that the long, black, velvety strips and the yellow ones on the sides shone in the golden sun. They wriggled down slowly, then they began crawling on the ground, a thick, black and yellow and brown blanket of bugs crawling to the Wabash River. In they went, and soon the yellow water was covered with a wriggling mass, and soon they were no more in sight.

Then the good people of Vincennes raised their voices and sang the praises of the Lord and their bishop. And the bishop thanked the Lord Jesus and added:

"Good Lord, because the people of this town are God-fearing and follow Your ways I pray You to keep them ever from this kind of pestilence and from the wild winds that tear down trees and houses. Save their food and their homes from destruction."

And the Lord heard Bishop Bruté's plea. Never have their crops been ravished, and when fierce tornadoes come that way, the wild winds break in two when they reach Vincennes, passing by on either side and never doing harm to that town.

The three sisters told me many more tales worth telling, and some day I will.

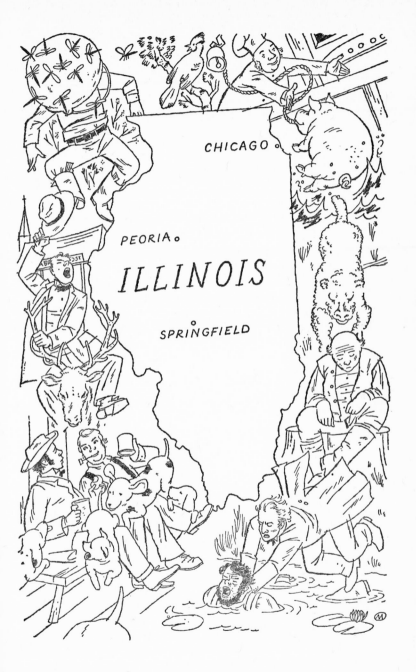

CHICAGO o

PEORIA o

ILLINOIS

o
SPRINGFIELD

Sand in the Bag

HERE'S a tale of Cairo, in Egypt in the southern part of Illinois. Folks said that town was like Sodom and Gomorrah for murder and for wickedness, that its people had eaten the bread of affliction and had drunk the wine of violence, and that their crimes were crimson, as it says in the Bible. But, truth to tell, these were silly lies spread by sharp and jesting tongues. Cairo folks were no worse than those of other towns, and they lived the same kind of life that others lived, and here's a tale to prove it.

It's the story of John Harmon and Mose Harrel, and it's as good a laughing tale as you'll find anywhere.

Mose worked in his brother's store, where they sold everything from nails to calico. It was a homey place, and near everybody came there, but most of all it was a favorite place of all the men who believed that talking work was doing work. They came to that place and did enough jaw crunching to tire an old woman.

Sometimes Mose didn't mind this. But at other times, when he had to tend to work, he found the long bleating a-hindering 'm.

135

One time he had to see what was in the place before ordering new supplies, and the dozen men sitting around the stove were in the way. He told this to his friend Harmon, who had a nimble mind, and the two made up a trick that would drive those drones away.

Late that day, when the sun was near setting and the full regiment of chin singers were around the hot stove swapping yarns, John Harmon came in with a tied-up bundle under his arm. In it were a couple o' pounds of sand.

"I need some shot," cried John when he came in. "Am goin' huntin' and I got plenty o' fast black powder right here in this bundle," and he pointed to the sand under his arm. "But I have no shot. Got some, Mose?"

"Sure got it. How much do you want?"

"Plenty. Weigh me out a couple o' pounds. Got no money with me right now, but I'll pay you comin' week."

"Sorry, Mister Harmon, we got t' get cash for goods here."

"What kind of place is this?" bellowed John. "Here I have enough powder to blow up your store and every house around "—with that he raised the bag of sand under his arm—"and you won't sell me any shot. Don't trust me? Don't you think I'm honest?"

"Reckon ye are, but I got t' get paid for what ye buy here."

"I'll pay you in a couple o' days."

"Sorry, Mister Harmon. Can't oblige ye. No money, no shot."

John Harmon shouted: "You are a disgrace to Cairo. No wonder foreign folk talk about us the way they do. Shame on your head. Goll ding it! If I can't get any shot, I don't need any powder." With that he walked close to the red-hot stove, opened the door quick, and raised the bundle of sand high and flung it into the stove.

Shivering timbers! There was a roar from the crowd: "Don't!" But it was too late. Then there was a dashing through that door the like had never been seen in Cairo. Those men ran faster than rabbits, faster than wild horses. Only Mose and John were left behind, holding their sides with laughter.

Now, you know, the farther the run, the longer the coming back. So Mose did his work without being bothered and John stayed there to help him.

John Harmon was a clever fellow, and many more tales are told of him. If you like to hear 'em, go and look for 'em.

Illinois River Tall Tale

THERE is no river in all the land more famous in song and story than the mighty "crooked river," the Illinois. There are songs and stories about the boats that floated in it and the men who rode those boats. For the ships and the men that manned them were as mighty as the river. Some of those stories are tall as the tallest. I'm going to tell you just one little one.

There was a grand steamer, the *Peoria*, a most elegant vessel in those days. That's what brass-mouthed Captain Keese said, that's what all the deck hands said, and that's what all the passengers said. And the loudest one to say it was the cook of that boat. There was no finer cook on all the river. Folks liked him better than any fancy French cook of which other boats boasted. Besides being a great cook, he was also a great fisherman.

He caught the finest and biggest fish in Illinois and cooked 'em the best and tastiest way. He was the kind who wasn't satisfied with ordinary bait like worms. "Worms 's good enough fer worms," he said. "I needs somethin' stronger; good, salted pig's meat's just right fer my kind o' fishin'. Pig's meat catches the finest fish in the Illinois."

One day a pig died on the boat and the cook didn't have the time to cut it up in pieces, so he put the whole animal on the stern cable on a strong meat hook and let it run in the water as bait.

The night was warm, and there was a fine company on the boat swapping tales and singing river songs. So the *Peoria* rode along in the yellow moonlight, while the dead pig rode in the yellow water.

Everybody, cook, crew, and passengers, forgot about that pig except the fishes. Nor did a soul think of that pig when all went to sleep.

Then, just as the stars were going out of the sky to go visiting, a queer thing happened. Suddenly that boat turned and twisted in all directions and then it began going backwards. It happened so quick not a man noted it.

The sun shone on the sparkling water so bright you couldn't look at it. Folks aboard awoke, rubbed their eyes, and looked out a-wondering. Men ran out half dressed, captain and crew stood at the rail not believing their eyes. The ship's cook ran out to the stern to see what had happened. And when he saw what he saw, his mouth and eyes opened doubly and he couldn't say a word. Such a sight had never been seen on the Illinois River!

The pig was gone! But on that meat hook was a cat-fish the size of a young whale! The barbels around his mouth were long as cattle whips. The catfish had swallowed the pig, body, feet, and tail, and it was now pushing the boat the other way, against the engine, trying to get home. It was pushing that boat, engine and passengers, as if it was a piece o' driftwood.

The cook just stood staring and staring at that monster, thinking he was dreaming. Then the cook and crew got back their wind.

"Cut the line," roared the captain.

"Not by fishhooks and worms!" yelled the cook. "That fish 'll make fine eatin'! Let's shoot 'm. We'll have fish an' line."

A gun was brought, and Captain Keese aimed straight and true while passengers and crew stood in admiration of the captain's courage.

He took a long time aiming, then—bang! crash! and no end of echoes came from all sides like the firing of a regiment of cavalry. The shot went true. The catfish turned his eyes, big as church glass windows, sadly at the folks on board, turned over, and pushed the *Peoria* no more.

There was shouting and joy aboard. The fish was hauled up, the captain turned the boat in the right direction. It went the way it had been going before, and passengers and crew ate catfish all the way home and sang "Old Zip Coon" and talked of the catfish big as a buffalo.

The Dance at
Hickory Creek

ONE time, in the olden days, folks at Hickory Creek, not far from Chicago, were making ready for a grand dance and fine frolic. Young women worked through small hours fixing their homemade fineries and the young fellows weren't far behind 'em. All were making ready for a ball spanglorious as any in Chicago.

To make it the best ever, the ladies of the settlement decided to invite a few young bachelor blades from Chicago, the big town on Lake Michigan.

The invitations were written and were sent by hand, and three young men from the best families accepted and said they'd be pleased, indeed, to come.

They got ready their most fashionable clothes, and since they had no horses of their own, they borrowed some from their friends and set out gaily for the grand ball at Hickory Creek.

When the three got there, Gholsen, Medard, and Kinzie, they were received like princes. First, their fine horses with shining saddles were put in the stable and were fed well and watered plenty. Then the masters were also treated to the best, and in the end their hostess took 'em down where the fiddlers and belles and beaux of Hickory Creek were ready for the ball.

Now, I must tell you the settlers of Hickory Creek were simple folk who worked hard in their fields and at their trades earning an honest living. They had no fancy clothes and they had no fancy manners. They were just plain, honest people, and when they came to that ball they came dressed in plain, honest clothes. Maybe some of the young ladies hankered after dresses bought from France or England, but most were satisfied with what they had, and that was true of the young fellows, too.

When the three Chicagoans entered, dressed in the latest fashion, there was a craning of necks and turning of heads, a primping and clutching of handkerchiefs or maybe even a fan to beat Jerusalem. Every girl's eyes were on those three young blades, and her mother's as well. Next came introductions and scraping and bowing and howdys and smiles and little blushes, just as there's always been since the days young folks first danced together.

But not all was joy and fluttering. There was another kind o' feeling running round in that ballroom. A feeling cold as a winter morning and angry as a screaming wind in empty branches. That's exactly the kind o' feeling the young men at Hickory felt in their inners.

From the minute those three Chicago dandies came in, it seemed as if all of the Hickory Creek boys were in

Samaria in the Bible. The girls just didn't look at 'em, they looked through 'em, and the young fellows didn't like that one bit—no, not one bit. That stormy feeling of anger grew like weeds as the hours went along.

The three city fellows were dancing all evening with the prettiest girls and the best dancers, and the young home fellows looked on with black looks. There was no open wailing or gnashing of teeth, but there was plenty growling talk and razor figuring. And so the evening hours went on, gay for the Chicago bachelors but gloomy for the Hickory Creek boys.

It was way past midnight when some of those Hickory Creek boys thought it was high time to do something, not just sit around mourning like at a funeral. Some o' them did a little quiet talking, and then a few went out into the starry, cold night straight into the stable. Pretty soon another fellow came in with a rusty pair of iron shears. At once they got to work.

Hair from manes and tails of the three smart Chicago dandies' horses began falling right and left like Philistines of old. It took a time, for the shears were none too sharp and the cutting was more zigzagging than a steep mountain trail. When they were done the horses' manes and tails looked ugly as mud-covered alligators' backs. Those horses were just no sight fit for a horseman or anyone else. When the town boys were done they went in to watch the city dandies dancing with their gals.

All good things and bad ones, too, have an ending, and so did the ball. The three, happy with the mighty con-

quests and "polite" sparking, thanked the blushing belles
and flushed mothers and promised to come again. They
bade a warm good night to all and went to the door ex-
pecting to find their horses brought to them, as they had
been taken away, by the friendly town boys. But no
horses were there, only the fading stars on the way to
visit one another. So they walked slowly to the stable to
fetch their animals. They were a little tired from dancing all the evening.

In the stable they saw many horses by the light of the
lantern, but not their horses. They walked from stall to
stall, coming back each time to the three horses that
looked like animals from another place of creation. Suddenly Bob Kinzie stopped, looked closely at the critters,
and cried out: "Them is our horses—I know 'em by the
saddles!"

For a long time the three stood there and not a word
came out o' them. But in the end the three saw these
were their horses, and they understood full well the trick
that had been played on 'em—and maybe why. Still they
had no words. They had borrowed these horses from
their best friends, and one a military man! Not a mumbling came from any of 'em.

Gholsen, he just had tears in his eyes, for he was soft at
heart; Medard was the first to say a word, but he only
mumbled, "Well, that horse ain't mine! It's Lieutenant
Foster's horse. Lord! what will he say?" But Bob Kinzie,
who was strong and hotheaded, cried he'd beat up that

whole puddly one-horse town, but no one was around. Maybe that's why he said it.

They rode home slowly on their strange-looking critters not saying much. Maybe they were a little wiser and thought folks had to pay for pleasure.

Lots of folks often find coming home from a party is not near as nice as going to it.

The Good Dogs and the Good Assessor

IN the olden days folks were restless rovers. No sooner would they settle in a place and a neighbor would come within fifty miles than they'd tie up their 'plunder,' which was how they called their few belongings, and go look for another spot.

The higher the cherries, the redder they look.

That's just the way Michael Kitterman, living in Indiana, thought, though he was a brainy man and broad and big-hearted, too.

He packed up the things that were his, and his neighbors bade him Godspeed. Said he, with a warm, big smile: "If we never see each other again, don't think it's too long a time. The sun 's always shinin' and the grass 's always green, and the good Lord on high watches over us never endin'." They were sorry to see him go.

So he came to Bureau County in Illinois, and settled in the rich lands, and grew rich in life and comfort.

It was the custom in those days, in that county, for the assessor, the man who decided how much tax each person had to give to pay for the running of the county government, to come to each settler during the warm summer days, look at what the settler had, and tell him how much he would have to pay. Sometimes the assessor put a tax on the queerest kind o' possessions—even on the dogs. Each family had to pay so much on every dog they had 'round the farm or house.

Most of the families in those days had many dogs, and nobody liked to pay a tax on 'em, though they didn't mind paying it on other things. So each settler kind o' warned the nearest neighbor to hide the dogs when the assessor was on the way.

One day a neighbor rushed to Michael Kitterman, warning him the assessor was coming to his house.

Michael Kitterman had thirteen dogs, and he loved all of 'em. He called 'em and got 'em down the cellar and gave 'em some bones. Then he locked the cellar door, never telling a soul what he had done. He was the kind who didn't believe in overspeaking himself.

Soon, after the hot sun stood highest, Assessor Payne came through the gate right into the house.

Payne and Kitterman were old friends, and the business of assessing was soon finished. Then, in sort of an offhandish manner, Payne asked about the dogs.

Michael answered kind of offhandish, too, saying there might be some 'round, the young'uns always played with 'em, but he had no notion 'bout it.

Payne smiled and said nothing. They both sat down on the porch, and Mistress Kitterman brought up a fine

mess of apples and a full pitcher of cool, pale-yellow
hard apple cider. Soon another neighbor came along, and
the three men sat eatin' red apples and drinkin' pale-
yellow hard apple cider and talking. They were begin-
nin' to feel warm all over, and their tongues were loose as
wiggling eels.

They were telling stories about how clever fellows
gain their ends by clever tricks.

Pretty soon the pitcher of good cider was drained to
the bottom and Michael called one of his sons to fetch
another from the barrel standing in the cellar. The fresh
cider Michael had been drinkin' had put clear out of his
mind that the cellar was full of dogs.

Michael's son, knowing nothing about the dogs,
opened the cellar door wide to go down and—out fled
thirteen barking, yelping dogs happy to be let out in
God's good sunshine.

They rushed wildly to their master, frisking, wagging
their tails, barking joyfully, jumping all over 'm, pawing
and licking him and the two other men.

Michael just got a little more red in the face, smiled
sheepishly, but never said a word. The two men grinned
and then let loose a good laugh but kept their mouths
buttoned. Not a man spoke till Michael shouted, "Son,
git that cider."

The boy who had been standing at the cellar door, not
knowing what to make of it, now rushed down and soon
came back with the pitcher full. Mistress Kitterman
brought another plate of hard red apples, and the men,

eating and drinking, began talking about crops and Lincoln and Douglas and their neighbors—but not a word was said about them dogs that were now running all over.

And Michael Kitterman paid no tax on dogs that summer.

Preacher Peter and
Mike Fink

PETER CARTWRIGHT was the greatest preacher of the State of Illinois. His tongue was sharp as a bull-whacker's whip, he was more clever than a fox, and he was strong as a bear. Wherever he came on his big strong horse, his broad white Quaker hat on his shaggy head, folks were glad to see him, glad to hear him preach God's word, and glad to see him put unbelievers and troublemakers in their proper place.

And, as ever is the American way, folks told and still tell tales about him. Psalms of tales, of deeds, and sayings. Some of these stories really happened and some just grew wild around him, but no matter what kind of a story it is, it always tells the kind of a man he was and how folks felt about him.

Now, here's one of those stories, but first I must tell you what the great preacher looked like—it will help you understand how he could do what he did.

He was not a tall man, no taller than other men, but thickset like a bull, and his shoulders were broad and strong. His muscles were hard as hickory, and he had a wild shock of hair around his sunburned face, and piercing eyes.

Round and round and up and down he rode on his big strong horse, preaching the golden gospel and keeping folks smiling by his wits. Whenever words and wit were not enough, he'd help along with strength of arms.

No matter where he went preaching, he always came back to Horse Creek, proud that he was a Sangamon River man.

Now, there was another riverman who was famous in Illinois and in all the land as well, around whom were woven even more tales than around Preacher Cartwright. That riverman's name was Mike Fink, and folks said of him he was half bad and half good, just as he said he was half horse and half alligator.

Both these men rode up and down the states and all around and so they were bound to meet time and time again, and you may be sure they had many scorching arguments loud enough to be heard for miles around.

One day these two met and words flew from each like fire sparks from an anvil. Mike, swearing and shouting, and Preacher Peter shouting, too, but only the words of the Lord. With every breath Mike Fink's words were getting more sulphury. In the end, Preacher Cartwright roared out if he didn't cease his black words and his worse life right soon, he'd baptize him in the river in the name o' the Devil.

Soon after, Preacher Peter was fishing with his sons,

Matt and Valentine, for pike, red horse, and big biting catfish, when along came Mike Fink.

Mike was feeling cantankerous and looking for trouble. No sooner did he see the preacher than he began shouting and bullying. Preacher Cartwright wasn't the man to take such words and gave him back in kind. Pretty soon the words were hot enough to broil the fish in the river and loud enough so the deaf fish could hear 'em.

Mike was swearing to make black crows blush white, and Peter Cartwright was roaring for him to stop his devilish language and say the Lord's Prayer instead or he'd send him where the willows were weeping all the time. But that just made Mike swear fiercer. Cartwright kept on roaring for him to stop and say the Lord's Prayer or he'd feed him to the fishes. Mike got worse. Before you knew, both of 'em were at each other with wildcat eyes and straining muscles. They were tearing each other and pulling and rolling on the ground. Seemed as if the preacher was trying to pull the boatman to the river. So they kept it up, with the crowd yelling and cheering and sweat pouring down the fighters' faces, neither seeming to win, but getting nearer and nearer to that yellow Sangamon River.

Out of the sunny sky and quick as swallows shooting down, Peter had Mike under the shoulders and swung him into the water. For strong belief gives power stronger than strength to muscles.

"Stop yer swearin' and mend your ways an' begin by

sayin' the Lord's Prayer right now," thundered the preacher so you could hear him as far as Springfield.

Mike, his head out of the water for a second, cried, gulping, "Ain't a-goin' to ef all the devils. . . ." Peter pushed hard, and down went Mike's head under the water. Then he let off, and the boatman's head bobbed up again.

Again Cartwright asked if he'd give up his ungodly life and say the Lord's Prayer. Mike answered in words so red and blistery it would have made that river boil if it hadn't been flowing all the time. Down went Mike's head again. So it kept on for a time, the preacher shouting for Mike to say the Lord's Prayer and Mike only answering with cuss words . . . till Mike seemed to have so much muddy water in him, he thought it was time to get a little clean religion. Next time the preacher let his head come up, he gurgled, "Come ye . . . preacher, I'll say the Lord's Prayer."

Wild Mike Fink said the Lord's golden prayer that day, and 'twas Preacher Cartwright made him say it. That's what folks tell around Salem in Illinois.

Giant Skeeters in the Brass Pot

THIS is a tale Guyla Moreland of Mound heard from her mother, who heard it from her mother, who may have heard it from her mother when she was stung by the first mosquito she met in the new land of America. That's the way stories travel, and that's how this one 'll travel from this book.

There was a man and woman had done their harvestin' and were busy puttin' away things for the long winter months, with the woman doin' most o' the work. It was that kind of a house. The man liked to make lip music and sleep like a lazy hound, while the woman, she liked to work, order the man about, and scold like a magpie.

One day that woman looked at her bin full o' crab apples and reckoned it 'd be a good idea t' cook 'm down to apple butter. Thought the next morning 'd be a good time t' begin, so she said to her lazy husband sittin' 'round:

"Aaron," she said, "jest go over to Mrs. Beegle an' borrow the brass pot. Got all them crab apples t' cook

154

and brass pot's better 'n the iron pot I got. Brass don'
take no scorchin'."

Aaron, he unfolded his long legs from under the rungs
of his seat leanin' against the wall, got up kind o' slow,
and said, "Waal, my right foot ain't itchin' and I don't
want t' start no journey, but seein' 's I ain't got nothin'
to do, I reckon I'll go. It's a long way."

Then he ambled off, pickin' up each leg as if it was a
load o' logs, while his old, black, skinny coon hound kept
close t' 'm.

When they passed the good old black iron kettle sittin' there on the black smoked ring, Aaron stopped to
take a rest. Then he said to the kettle and his hound:

"We brought this here kettle alon'side with the other
cookin' iron that was good 'nuf fer us folks in yonder
days. Now black iron ain't good 'nuf fer wimin. Gotta
walk clear acrost Boar Creek swamp to borry an ol' brass
kettle. Wimin's got notions."

Blue, the old hound, twitched his ears and wagged his
tail, slinkin' along the grass. He knew every word his
master was sayin'.

'Twas long walkin', miles, over hills, through dales,
and across swamps. Took time. When he got to the
Beegles there was talk 'bout the borrowin', talk with the
blacksmith, and a drink o' milk kept cold in the spring.
Took time, and 'twas gettin' kind o' late when Aaron
set his legs an' nose homeward.

Walkin' wasn't easy and that brass kettle was mighty
heavy. Weighed near ten pounds to drag on the arm.

The sun was gettin' low, and the night insects were comin' out for rompin' round.

Jest as he was gettin' near the swamp, Aaron heard a great buzzin'. Buz-z-z-z! That noise was big 'nuf to drown out the tree frogs hollerin' and the katydids shrill-in'. It was the biggest buzzin' Aaron ever heard.

Pretty soon, whang! something strong hit 'm and wow! stung 'm deep. He gave it a big slap with his big hand, but he missed by a mile.

Another came at 'm, and another, and another. They was comin' thick 's hail an' big 's blackbirds. One, big 's a pigeon, seemed t' be the leader directin' 'em where to sting.

They was after his old coon hound, too. Blue, he let out a fierce yelpin', for one had stung 'm on the nose. His tail dropped and he began runnin' like a scared rabbit straight for home.

Aaron felt like a drownin' man in his clothes who couldn't swim. He looked round 'm wild and scared, but his legs, they just couldn't move. Without even thinkin', he put that ten-pound kettle on his head. Now his legs felt good and began movin', and he even laughed under his kettle coverin', thinking how he had fooled them bloody skeeters and how they couldn't do 'm no harm now.

The skeeters, seein' the kettle and no head t' sting, were madder 'n wild bulls. They were buzzin' and buz-zin' and buzzin'. Sounded pretty, like a great water fallin' down over rocks. But Aaron, he kept on walkin' and laughin'.

Then, out of a clear sky, Aaron heard a queer sound—like metal bitin' metal. He walked a little faster, kind o' worryin' what new trouble was on the way. He was walkin' fast and listenin' close.

The noise was gettin' louder, and he looked up cross-eyed-like to the place where it was a-comin' from. Jerusalem cricket! 'Twasn't 's dark 's it had been just a minute ago. Now there was holes there 'bout large as a nail's head, lettin' in the light and showin' the skeeter stinger bill inchin' through that brass kettle and aimin' straight at his forehead.

He let out a devilish screech and sent his fist flyin' inside that kettle and bradded that skeeter stinger bill with one wallop. Skeeter was now stuck good and fast.

But now he heard hammerin' all around. There was another skeeter stinger bill! And another! And another! They was comin' on right and left. Quick 's they came, Aaron let his big fists fly and bradded 'em. Then, all of a sudden, that kettle lifted off his head! It was the bradded skeeters liftin' it. Aaron swore for the rest of his life he heard that leader skeeter big 's a pigeon laughin' at 'm and givin' a loud buzzin' order. For right after, the other skeeters thick 's fog went at 'm, like wolves for raw meat. The attack put the fear of the Lord in his heart and the strength of Samson in his legs. He let loose in a wild run 'd 've done honor to a stag chased by dogs. He hadn't run like that in forty years, and he just

kept on goin' and goin', his tongue hangin' out like Blue's
while the skeeters were stingin' 'm fierce 's wildcats. His
breath was pretty near all gone, his legs was like lead,
and his swollen head felt on fire when he fell across the
doorsteps of his cabin.

Aaron's wife, mad fit t' kill from waitin', took one
look at what fell in the room, didn't recognize 'm, he
looked so queer, got the brush broom restin' in the
corner, and began beatin' that swollen head. She just
didn't know Aaron from Adam's off ox.

"Lay off beatin' me over the head where the skeeters
near stung me to death. It's Aaron, yer ol' man."

"Ef'n yer Aaron, where's the brass kettle I sent ye
fer?" she shrilled.

He looked up the best he could. Puffin' hard, he told
her how them skeeters had attacked him and how he had
bradded the stinger bills and how they had flown off,
leavin' the rest to eat 'm up.

She saw his head and saw his eyes and she knew he
spoke gospel. So she rubbed his head with bear's grease
and penny royal till he felt all better.

From that time she never hankered for what her
neighbors had but was satisfied with her own.

The Governor and the Cannon

RUSHVILLE in Illinois is a fine town for fine boom-ing-cannon tales. Even the name of that town makes a swishing cannon-shot sound. Rushville! Maybe that's why they tell cannon-shot tales about the place.

It happened in the days of Governor Ford, who loved big booming jokes like fat Falstaff, the Englishman of old about whom Shakespeare wrote.

There had been argufying and battles between the Mormon and the Nauvoo and other folks around, and the good governor decided to go there and give those hotheads a cooling bath. He came out with a company of militia to quell those rioting lunkheads and on their way they passed through Rushville. The citizens wel-comed the governor and his men right properly and they camped them in the village square.

Now it so happened that the governor could not sleep that night, like King Ahasuerus. He was worried about those folks who couldn't live peacefully together though they believed in the same God in a different way. He tossed around from right to left, counted sheep, and when everything failed he decided the best thing was to get up and keep busy.

The round, silvered moon rushed wild through small, torn clouds and it was so light you could read a book. But the governor's mind wasn't on reading, he just wanted those night hours to pass away quick. And when they wouldn't, he decided to practice pistol shooting.

Maybe that wasn't the right time for such a thing, but Governor Ford never thought of that. He set up a target on the fence of James Little's house that was on the town square and began banging bullets in the still hours, making enough noise to waken the fish on the bottom of Lake Erie.

Mister Little was as good a sleeper as any, but soon the banging awoke him. First he thought it was Indians on the warpath attacking the town. He rushed out in his long white nightshirt and white nightcap and saw it was the Governor of the State of Illinois making that terrible noise. Now, Mister Little was a patriotic American citizen and he felt he had as good a right as any governor in all the world to sleep at the right and proper time. He was madder than all the hornets of North America. He stopped long enough to put on his cowhide boots and then ran straight to the sheriff, woke him, and told him the governor was clear out of his mind and without consideration for the peace of his fellow citizens. He also said it was a misdemeanor to disturb folks in the middle of the night and there was a law against it, and there was a fine for shooting firearms in the village proper, and many other things too hard to write. In the end he swore a warrant against the governor and had him served with it.

Now morning came pretty quick for Governor Ford, for he was madder than a baited bull. He came before the justice and had to pay a fine, and he swore a blood-bound oath he'd come back and pay that town back in kind at the right and proper time.

Governor Ford and his militiamen went to Nauvoo, ended the riots, and then turned their steps homeward to Springfield. But all the time he was figuring how to get even with Rushville for the indignity they put on 'm.

Now, it so happened that the head of the State of Illinois and his militiamen approached Rushville in the middle of the night. It was still, and a sickle of a moon looked young and surprised in the sky. Then Governor Ford had a thought so good he wouldn't have sold it for the presidency of the United States.

He ordered his men to march quietly and not to make a sound. When they got to the town square he ordered the artillerymen to set up their cannons next to James Little's house right under his window, load 'em to the hilt, and point 'em skyward so no harm 'd be done, and . . . fire away.

Everything was done as the governor ordered and all the men stood around in silent attention. Then the chief of the Sucker State hissed low, "Fire!" Off went those cannons and it sounded as if all the state was being torn to pieces.

Next, good Governor Ford shouted: "Forward march, in double-quick time." Going as fast as they could, the governor at the head, the military of the state were out of Rushville mighty quick. If Governor Ford hadn't felt fully the dignity of his office, he would have yelled and whooped with joy.

James Little and the rest of the Rushville folk fell out of their beds as if the last Day of Judgment had come. They rushed out, shouting and crying, each trying to find out what had happened. When they saw the moving soldiers in the distance, they understood it was Governor Ford paying them for the fine they had made him pay.

> Chicken on the haystack,
> Hawk came flying by,
> Grabbed the chicken by the neck,
> And feathers began to fly.

And that's just what happens when you don't let a governor who can't sleep practice a little shooting in the middle o' the night.

Butting a Sermon

THE Lord has strange ways of teachin' folks the holy word, and I know the good Lord thinks a sermon preached with a laugh 's as good as a sermon preached with a long face.

In the early days of Illinois, when men had no time t' build churches as quick as they built cabins, preachers preached in the homes of different folks and the word of God was as sweet in the home as it was in a church. That's what Preacher Lee said as he went from home t' home spreadin' the word of the Lord.

One time he came to a family where there was a young 'un who loved animals more than his brothers or sisters. That little fellow could train the dumb beasts to do almost anything. He had a little lamb his father had given 'm. It was a frisky little beast, jumpin', buttin', playin' with the children as if it were a dog.

Pretty soon the little fellow had trained that lamb to butt like a goat every time he'd nod his head. The boy 'd just have to nod his head and the lamb 'd buck, head on, as good as any ram. It always brought a good laugh.

When Preacher Lee came to preach in that house, friends and neighbors came to hear the good word. Preacher Lee spoke like a man of God. He was tellin' 'bout the kingdom come, the kindness of the Lord, and how folks could sit beside 'm on high if they led a godly life on this earth. The words were sweet to the ear, like the singin' of the little birds in the trees.

In that settlement lived a man given to laziness an' drinkin'. His head was set on the wrong side.

That day, when everybody was listenin' to the golden words, that godless man was carryin' on as he always did. When he had enough or maybe too much in the inn and no one to argue with, he wandered around the roads.

Soon he heard the preacher's voice, and so he walked kind o' slow toward the house where Brother Lee was exhortin' folks to live in the way of the Lord. The fellow looked in the door with thick eyes an', seein' no seat, sat himself on a wooden stump that was right outside the door. He didn't get many of the fine words, for he felt heavy an' sleepy an' his head fell down on his chest kind o' drowsin'. Every time the preacher raised his voice, his head went up awakin' with a start. But soon he was drowsin' again, his head droopin' on his chest.

The little pet lamb, wanderin' around nibblin' grass and hearin' the preacher's voice, came near. There at the door was a man . . . noddin' his head up an' down, up an' down. Just the kind of noddin' its master had taught it to mean buttin'. But it wasn't his own master noddin', this was a stranger, so the lamb stopped an' looked on for a time.

There he was, doin' it again . . . an' again. Sure it meant buttin', even though it was not the master doin' it. The next time that fellow's head came up an' went down, that lambkin made a flyin' run, hittin' the fellow straight in the droopin' head. Down he went, rollin' an' rollin' over the ground. Well, that congregation let out a roarin' laugh ye could hear as far as Mexico. Preacher Lee tried his best to keep a straight an' sober face, but it was no use. He just had to join the congregation, and when it all quieted down he said with a twinkle in his eye: "I hope that man 'll never forget the sermon preached 'm by a lamb o' the Lord. For the Lord has many ways to teach folks in this world, and the one to bring a laugh 's good as one to bring a tear.

Oh, whip the devil around the stump
And hit him a crack at every jump.

Springfield Got It

IN the states of our land, in the counties, there was ever friendly rivalry and arguments which town should be the county seat where the laws should be made. Sometimes battles were fought with fists and words thick as carrier pigeons; sometimes battles were fought with jokes and clever tricks.

When Sangamon County, a singing word in the winds of Illinois, was to choose its county seat there was almighty rivalry between the young town of Springfield and also the very young town of Sangamo that was not very far away.

Folks with beards and full of flaming oratory in Sangamo made grand speeches telling all the world that if Sangamo town would be the county seat it would shine like a golden star on the horizon of the state full of golden corn.

Folks in Springfield sang just as grandilious chin music. If Springfield would become a county seat it would give the great, rich prairie state of Illinois roots reaching to the end of the earth and enrich all the world.

So it went on back and forth, each outshouting the other until the almighty legislative body of the state made up to examine the two towns and decide which was the better as the county seat for the Garden of Eden of the West, the State of Illinois.

On a windy, sunny day when birds were making summer holiday, the members of that committee set out on horseback from Vandalia to Springfield to examine that town.

They rode and argued as is ever the way of men bent on making a decision. So they came to the little town of Springfield in the valley of the Sangamon River with soft, rolling prairie lands.

There was a grand reception for the men of Vandalia by the farmers and mechanics and merchants of the settlement. There were big words and bigger promises, but in the end the committee, being honest men, said it was only fair to examine Sangamo Town before making up their minds.

Springfield men scratched their heads and spoke among themselves and tried to figure how to stop that committee from going to Sangamo Town. Then up spoke Andrew Elliot, the finest guide around those parts, and said he'd guide the committee in a way they'd never choose that settlement for the county seat.

He went to the committee and told 'em it was a long ride and a hard ride and there was no road to Sangamo Town, but he, Andrew Elliot, knew every blade of grass and every tree and would guide 'em safely to that distant place. The men were glad of that, for the riding from Vandalia to Springfield had been long and hard and they had lost their way many a time.

Now, Sangamo Town was only a short seven miles as the crows fly from Springfield and Andrew knew that well, but the members of the committee did not.

They set out the next morning under a cloudy sky, Andrew leading 'em.

Instead of taking the road which he knew well, he went round and round. He led them through tangling woods and through oozing bogs. He twisted 'em through swollen creeks and whipping trees. He led 'em over deer tracks and through six-foot-high cutting grass, and as they rode and their horses' legs were stained by wild berries the members of that committee lost their temper and lost their patience. They never heard the laughter of the gobbling turkeys and the twittering birds, they never heard the humming in the leaves, they were too busy grumbling and complaining. When they got to Sangamo Town, tired and draggy, they gave the place just a glance, and it was the only glance that place got for a county seat. All these men wanted was to get back to Springfield as quick as their horses would carry them.

Andrew, smiling, led them back through pathless woods and swamps all over again. And so they came back to Springfield, where awaited them warm food and good rest. And when they had both, they decided Springfield was the right and proper place for a county seat, since

Sangamo Town was so hard to reach. Andrew smiled and never said a word.

Springfield was chosen as the county seat, and a wise choice it was. The town grew quick and large, so large that in the end it was made the capital of the state.

As for Sangamo Town, folks began moving away from there, and soon it was lost in the shadows of things gone in the land, except in folks' stories, the kind I just told you.

The White Mule
From the Other World

THERE lived in Albion a man who pondered so hard, he hadn't time to think. That's why he didn't believe in God. He didn't believe in God even though he saw all around him the miracles of beauty no one but He could create. And birds and butterflies and flowers grew on just the same.

Friends and preachers argued with him enough to fill a river with words, but it changed him as much as sticking a little finger in a rushing stream to change its running water.

The years rolled over his head, his hair turned gray and white, and do you think that changed him? No, not even the size of a snowflake. Fact is, he became worse, and folks had given up trying to change that heathen sinner.

On went the days of his life, his back became bent and his eyes turned dim, but the spirit of that man revolting against the Lord was as strong as ever. Instead of making his peace with men and God, he scoffed at believers. He made jest of all things sacred, spoke blasphemous words, and kept on shouting there was no other world of which the Bible tells.

"Ef there is another world," he roared, "I'll be comin' back 's an all-white mule. An' take heed ye treat me proper an' feed me plenty, else I'll plague ye t' beat the burnin' fires o' hell, as a mule from the other world kin. But I tell ye there ain't no other world, and I'll never come back here as a mule or any other way."

Some friends and neighbors laughed, many were angry at these black words and shook their heads and said that fellow and the Devil were drinking from one and the same cup. But each and every one promised under oath to feed 'm well if he returned as a mule to tell there was another world besides the one he lived in.

So time went on, and talk went on, and in the end the same thing happened that always happens. One morning Albion folks awoke and found that man who didn't believe in God nohow had gone the long, long way where mules went to buy horns.

Even though he didn't believe in the Lord, kind folks gave him a decent Christian burial.

There was much talk of him on Sundays and at home around the table and at the fields at work. That unbelieving man said he'd come back as a white mule if there was a life in the world he'd gone to, and everybody was watching, waiting, and talking.

One fine day, lo and behold! there came to Albion a

strong mule, ALL WHITE! There wasn't a hair or a speck of any other color on that mule.

So there *was* another world! The unbeliever came back as a white mule to prove it, as he said he would in jest and scoffing. Folks looked and marveled.

Then tongues were let loose. There was a lesson for scoffers! Was that mule sent to teach a lesson? Or was it a sign of anger? Or maybe that mule was the unbeliever himself, turned to a four-footed beast to punish him for his scoffing words. Whichever way the argument ran, there was that white mule, real as the road under foot, braying loud for food and drink. Maybe it was reminding Albion folks in mule language of the promise they had made—to feed the white mule that returned to prove there was another world.

So folks gave that animal plenty of oats in the winter and the best of pastures in the summer, and it lived a life that many a poor man envied.

And whenever a scoffer of the Bible came along, he'd be told the tale of the man who came back as an all-white mule to prove there was another world.

To this very day this tale is told by folks in Albion, and that is how come I tell it to you.

All's Well
That Ends Well

THIS happened in Chicago a long time ago and folks still like to tell the story. For anything that brings a laugh is always good to hear.

There lived then a man named George Wandall, who believed a lucky man can get eggs from a rooster. He owned a little stand where he sold vegetables the farmers brought from the neighboring farms. But more hogs and cattle came to his stand for vegetables and fruits than folks, and so he began thinking hard of something else by which he could earn an honest living!

"There's no money in fresh, sweet-smellin' strawberries, apples, or greens. Got to think o' somethin' folks like better."

So he set his mind a-working how he could earn a living good 's any man, and once George set his mind a-working something was sure to come out in the end. He thought and he thought, but nothing came to 'm till one day when he was talking to a man going out West. That man just happened to speak of foreign lands and said he'd seen a zoo full of animals in the city of London, the capital of England, and that most of those animals had come from our own land.

"By Gor! that gives me a fine idea," cried George. "Here in Chicago, I'm gonna start a zoo. I'm gonna get plenty o' wild animals, and folks 'll pay plenty o' money to see 'em. We got everything 's good 's England, and maybe better."

George was the kind o' man who didn't let the grass grow under his feet. He sold his stand and built a big shed on State and Randolph streets. It was a big field closed around with an eight-foot fence and canvas over it and the inside was divided up to house the animals that were coming.

After that he went to St. Louis to buy the beasts. He found 'em there a-plenty. So he bought a wolf and a bear; a deer and a raccoon; a squirrel and a guinea pig; a horned frog and a horned owl; and a monkey and an elk. That sure enough was plenty of animals to start a zoo in any place.

He loaded 'em on wagons and in good time brought 'em to Chicago to his eight-foot-high zoo, and put each in a separate place by itself. When they were all safe, he spread the news through all the town that he had a zoo fine as London and he was waiting for all to come and see it. George himself sat at the gate to collect the money folks would pay to see his show.

Now it so happened a few young Chicago blades were

sitting in a coffeehouse talking of this and that. Just about when they felt like hugging cinnamon bears and dancing with full-grown alligators, along came the news that the new zoo was ready for visiting. The young gentlemen, feeling gay as lords, cried: "To George Wandall's brand new zoo we go to say howdy and shake hands with the wild animals of the world."

They set out, singing *tralerilas* and tunes like "Nellie Gray" and the "Prairie Flower" till they came to Randolph and State streets, to the zoo of Wandall's wild animals.

There were flags and music and a good crowd. At the gate sat Mister Wandall with a white shirt and a black tie, smiling like he was being paid for it and asking for money of those who wanted to come and see the "Most Wonderful Show On Earth."

The young, gay Chicago sports had never thought o' that. Besides, they didn't want to see the animals, they wanted to shake hands with 'em.

"We didn't come t' pay, Mister Wandall," they cried, "we want to shake hands with the bear and feed nuts to the wild squirrels."

Mister Wandall replied he and his animals were highly gratified by the honor, but they'd have to pay just the same as other folks.

One word brought another, and soon the voices were louder and next thing you know the four gentlemen crashed past Mister Wandall without paying.

The high arguments and loud talk had raised the dander of the four, and instead of gentling the animals as they said they would, they bullyragged and baited 'em.

They poked 'em with sticks and put snuff under the wolf's nose. They kicked the bear and broke the hurdy-gurdy. When they had near wrecked the place, Doc Norman, one of the four, feeling like one of Old Scratch's crew, decided he had to ride the big elk with the brown eyes all 'round the town.

"Might 's well be ridin' while the fun's goin'," he shouted again and again.

He tried to mount the big animal, but the elk didn't seem to be wanting a rider. But the other three came to help and in the end he got on, holding tight to the horns. The elk balked and bounced and danced and then shot past George Wandall, out through the gate, into the streets of wild Chicago town.

They rode and careened and bounced and bumped along the streets and houses while Doc Norman's friends and half Chicago folks followed behind singing and shouting and making every other kind of noise. 'Twas as good 's fiddling and dancing, and all had the jolliest time ever. So they came to the coffeehouse from which the four had started off and Doc Norman rode that elk through the wide door, up the wide stairs, into the coffeeroom where men were sitting talking of the West and passing the merry cup.

Soon George Wandall came crying for vengeance and his property, and then Doc Norman and his friends, who were good fellows at heart, raised a fat purse and gave it to the zoo man, to pay for the hurdy-gurdy and the damage done. So in the end folks were happy all 'round, which is the way everything should end.

The Miller and the
Blue Jay

THERE was a miller had a mill right on a river. It was the best place for a mill, for the water did the work grinding grain for food to eat. But the miller who ran that mill loved hunting more than watching the mill. He loved hunting more than he loved friends or food.

One day a farmer brought a sack o' corn to that mill to put in the grist. He told the miller he'd leave the corn there, for he had to go on an errand for his wife, but he'd soon return to fetch the grain. He left the sack with the miller, mounted his horse, and went off.

The miller put the grist in the hopper and turned on the water and sat down waiting. The noise of that flowing water and maybe the song of the birds and insects made the miller sleepy, till he was awakened like by a cannon shot. But it was no cannon shot, only the gobbling of a wild turkey somewhere in the greening woods. That turkey seemed to be gobbling kind o' challengy for the miller to go and get 'm. That's what the miller thought.

Forgetting all about the mill or work, the miller ran to the cabin, got his gun, and ran out looking for that wild turkey.

Now, the birds and beasts had learned something about the settlers who had taken their land from them. Mostly the birds. The birds around the mill knew the habits of the miller as good as they knew their trees. They knew he did not tend his work properly and were ever watching for the grain they could gain from his carelessness.

A blue jay sitting nearby preening its gleaming feathers saw the miller run for his fowling piece and saw him running off.

That blue jay was a pretty smart bird, and though no one heard 'm say it, I'm sure he said to himself: "There goes that miller who never attends to his work as he should. And that gives me a fine chance for a good meal."

Flying and hopping that looked near dancing, the bird got to the wheel just when the corn began coming out.

The first kernel fell and the blue jay ate it quick. It tasted mighty fine. The next kernel came and he ate that. It tasted even better. The kernels kept on coming and the blue jay kept on eating. Maybe some of his blue jay friends came along and joined in the fine feast. Those golden kernels were gone quick as they came out.

The while the miller was looking for that wild turkey, but he couldn't find him anywhere, so he came back, his dander high as pine trees. When he saw the corn gone and the stones worn he said hard words high as heaven.

But the blue jay twittered a sweet song telling that miller exactly what he thought of 'm and thanking him for being a careless fellow so that he could have a fine feast.

The miller didn't understand a word the blue jay said, though he understood every word the farmer said when he asked for his corn. The miller had to pay for being careless in his work; the blue jay got a meal for keeping his eyes wide open. Now, who was the smarter of the two?

Help in Need and Abe in Deed

THIS is the kind of story that happened in the days when Americans were on the move to the West.

Cows think grass is greener in the next pasture, and men think the same. That's why Doctor Chandler of Rhode Island moved onward to Illinois. He was a clear-thinking man, honest and kind, and wherever he stopped on the way folks took to him. So he came to Sangamon Bottom and settled in the rich and sun-soaked bottom lands. He "entered" one hundred and sixty acres; that is, he applied for that much land, built himself a cabin of strong logs, and life was rich and exciting as wind and weather.

Now, it was the custom in the State of Illinois to allow each settler eighty acres more, if he wanted it, on both sides of his claim. These the settlers could "enter" and pay for whenever he had the money to pay. For any one else to buy these acres before the first settler had a full chance to pay for them was worse than horse stealing.

Not long after Doctor Chandler settled, along came a man named English, a porcupiny-like fellow who didn't like the sun because it was warm, didn't like the rain because it was wet, and didn't like the wind because it blows.

The doctor had a heart soft as the rich plowed earth in the Sangamon valley, so, wanting a neighbor, he offered half his claim of the eighty acres, to which he had a right, to English to settle near him as a good neighbor.

English's prickly face turned persimmony-puckered and he barked, since Dr. Chandler had not made his claim properly, *he'd* make it for these acres himself come earth and hellfire, and he went off at once to carry out his threat.

Doctor Chandler knew he'd have to enter his claim and pay for the land quick or he'd surely lose it.

He had only fifty dollars and he needed much more, so he got on his strongest horse, raced to his neighbor, told his tale and borrowed the money, and then he sped on to Springfield to the land office.

Neither Doctor Chandler nor his fine horse took a minute's rest. They went through woods and roads, through muddy creeks and cutting grass, and they were nearing Springfield and the land office. He was just about ten miles from town and his racing, steaming, and sweating horse was slowing up when there galloped up to him two young fellows. One of them was the peculiarest young man Doctor Chandler ever laid his eyes on. He was long-shanked and gangling, just kind of hanging together. He had a long and oldish sunburned face full of lines, and a long nose. His felt hat on his head was the color of Joseph's coat in the Bible; he had on homespun jeans, and his pantaloons were stuffed into his rawhide boots. Though he was a-horseback and looked half sleepy, you knew it was a kind of face that could also be angry as the clouds.

This queer-looking young stranger and his friend came up to Chandler and rode alongside of his foaming horse that had slowed up. The three got to talking and Doc Chandler, being openhearted, soon told his tale and then the talking face of that queer-looking stranger lit up like lashed lightning. He said to Chandler in a quiet way, but full of oaken strength, he wished English were here so he could talk to 'm. But since he wasn't, the best thing would be to beat him at his game. He offered to lend his own fresh horse to Chandler and he'd take the doctor's tired animal and give it back in Springfield. He added, he was a young surveyor come anew to town to earn his living.

Doctor Chandler thanked him warmly, said his own horse was rested by then, and he would go ahead.

The two bid him Godspeed and told him a road that would get him to town in no time.

The road they told him cut off near half of the riding and God was on the doctor's side. He reached the land office just before that land robber English came. If the strangers hadn't shown him the short cut to the town, he would never have gotten there on time. He entered his claim, paid his money, and set out for home, a happy man.

It wasn't long after, that Doctor Chandler needed a surveyor for his land. The county surveyor was busy from morn to night with the new settlers, and a neighbor told him of the new surveyor who he believed was even better than the county surveyor. Doctor Chandler asked his friend to send him to his place. When he came—why, it was none other than the peculiar-looking fellow who had saved his claim for the land of his farm. The doctor was truly happy to see him and return the kindness in deed. They got to talking in the friendliest way, and the young fellow told him his name was Abraham Lincoln. So did Abe Lincoln sow kindness and fairness wherever he went from his earliest days. Truly he came in deed when folks were in need.

The Roots of These Stories

INTO the telling of these tales have gone months of pleasant and profitable research both in books and among folks—the same kind of work that went into the telling of my other two books of folk stories, *New England Beanpot*, which consists of stories told in the six New England states, and *Upstate, Downstate*, containing stories heard in the five Middle Atlantic states.

To mention all the books I examined before I wrote *Sand in the Bag* would take too long and probably would not interest you. Such long lists of books are for folklore scholars, who are interested mainly in the "why's" and "wherefore's" and histories of stories.

It will be enough for you, good reader—who, I am sure, are interested, even as I am, in good yarns and in people—to know that nearly every book with anything in it pertaining to the three states of Ohio, Indiana, and Illinois, was read carefully. These included travel books, guides, and histories—histories of states, of rivers, of mountains, of churches, of villages thriving today and of villages now deserted. It included every county history—and there are eighty-eight counties in Ohio, ninety-two in Indiana, and one hundred and two in Illinois. The books I examined, you see, ran into the hundreds. For the state of Ohio alone there were two hundred and eighty-seven.

In addition, I read other publications, including every historical, archaeological, and folklore magazine in the three states, as well as every kind of magazine in which folklore material may wander. Railroad magazines, automobile magazines (such as that issued by the Ford Motor Company), and many other trade magazines; all were helpful. All these were not only examined but fine-combed by my wife and me for anything that would help in the finding and telling of a folk story. But more important than the research in printed matter was the correspondence and rivers of talk with folks now living who remember the simple life and the simple stories of yesteryear. All these men and women were eager to write and tell me personally about the days and stories of long ago. As a result, I have endless letters (some in writing difficult to decipher), disks and disks of recordings, and, above all, priceless memories of golden hours of conversation.

Among folklore scholars such persons are called "informants." Somehow the word does not fit, for it brings to mind conspiracies, courts, trials. True, folklore authorities use it merely to mean people who give information, but these folks do infinitely more than give information about a story—they tell of the life they have lived.

One of the finest Christians I have ever met was one of these "informants": the Reverend Austin Crist of Lima, Ohio. When I saw him he was ninety-one and a half, but his memory was crystal clear, and for nearly two hours he sang rainbows of songs and told me rich incidents of his life. These were fully as interesting as his stories.

Then there was Mr. Lewis B. Richardson of Trafalgar, Indiana, poet and storyteller without compare, and Mr. Elmer Waters, of Lafayette, Indiana, in the same class. There was District School Superintendent Grover Brown, of Nashville, Indiana, and Fred Marshall of Dayton, Ohio, and the Draim sisters of Vincennes, Indiana, and many others. To call these men and women "informants" is calling larks toads, though the toad is a perfectly nice animal—it is the name that is unsavory.

Giving my thanks to these folks in black words on white paper seems watery, but I know they will understand the gratitude I feel for the aid they have given me.

These are the names of a few who were the parents of these stories.

In Ohio, there were:

Mr. W. A. Amstutz, of Bluffton, a collector of stories himself.

Mr. W. C. Beer, Jr., of Bucyrus, whose tales could fill a book.

Reverend H. Barnes, of Kent, who told me countless stories, but there was room for only one, "The Tapping Ghost of Edinburg."

Mrs. C. J. Calmery, of Youngstown. Mr. Louis Cook, of Basil.

Mr. E. K. Core, of Bellefontaine. Mr. William Coyle, of Wittenberg College, Springfield.

Mrs. H. R. Collacott, of Painesville, who gave me reams of information on the way of life in her section.

Reverend Austin M. Crist, of Lima. For nearly two hours he sang old songs for me, told me about life in Ohio, related anecdotes and stories, among them "The Faithful Dog" and the John Brown story. (I heard this story almost identically from Mr. Richardson in Trafalgar, Indiana); also "The Immortal J.N." (he knew the immortal J.N.) and "The Witch of Ohio." *The Scioto Gazette* printed it, and it was reprinted in the Ohio Archaeological and Historical Publication, Volume XXXIII.

Mrs. H. B. Diefenbach, of Akron. Mrs. F. R. Donaldson, of Alliance.

Mr. G. Fitzgerald, of Dayton, who even asked the local newspapers to announce that I was looking for folk stories.

Mr. Andrew Franz, of Bath.

Mrs. Carl Goehring, of Steubenville.

Mrs. E. A. Goodman, Reference Librarian of the Youngstown and Mahoning County Public Library, was most generous and helpful with advice and material in general and with "The Sad Tale of Three Slavers" in particular.

Mr. A. F. Hardman of the Ohio Bell Telephone Company, Cleveland. Mr. G. Higley, of Youngstown. Gertrude Hassler, of Cleveland. Mrs. F. C. Holbrook, of Cincinnati. Mr. E. D. Howard, of Columbus.

Miss Ethel L. Hutchins, Head of the Reference Department of the County Library District of Hamilton County, Public Library of Cincinnati, gave me invaluable help.

Miss Louise M. Jones, of Medina.

Mrs. L. K. Keyser, of Dayton, who contributed some anecdotes which are gems.

Mrs. M. B. Longsworth, of Lima, who gave help and advice with the material of Allen County.

Miss Alma McCormick, of Gallipolis. Colonel D. McKell, of Chillicothe, whose excellent knowledge of the stories of Ross County was put at my disposal.

Mrs. G. A. Metzger, of Dayton. Mr. R. Mohler, of Akron. Miss Violet Morgan, of Hillsboro.

Mr. Watt P. Marchman, Director of the Hayes Memorial Library, of Fremont.

Mr. Fred Marshall, of Dayton, a fine historian and a mine of information about the lore and life and stories of the olden days. His memories, recorded or written down, would enrich our knowledge of the bygone life in Ohio in general and of Lucas County in particular. From the large amount of material he gave me, I chose "The Boy Who Would be Orator."

Mr. J. C. Pearson, of Cleveland. Mr. C. Pockrand, of Akron. Mrs. Metta Point, of Tallmadge. Mrs. B. D. Richardson, of Malta.

Miss Waive Ripple, of West Lafayette. Mr. C. G. Rust, of Springfield, who can tell as good stories as any man in the Hoosier State.

Mr. E. D. Rigney, of Chillicothe, who has the history and lore of his county at his finger tips and who has worked unceasingly to make his local historical-folklore museum one of the showplaces of the states. He told me many stories, including the Sky-Foogle.

Miss Pauline Riley, Secretary of the Knox County Historical Society, Mount Vernon, helped me with the "Seeley Simpkins" story. (I also heard it at a meeting of the Ohioana Library Society. Stories of men riding bulls instead of horses were quite common in the early days, and I heard them in other states. I found a particularly fine story of this type in Rhode Island.)

Mrs. Mildred Shepherst, of Toledo.

Mr. F. N. Schneider, of Zanesville, a scholar, a historian, and a folklorist who helped me to a better understanding of the Ohio scene and Ohio life and lore.

Mrs. W. E. D. Smith, a collector of folk stories and an author in her own right. She gave me advice and help with the story of Lottie Moon.

Mr. George W. Stratton, who likes to be known as a "Miller," of Flushing, most generously helped me with information and the charming story, "The House That Jack Built."

Mrs. Melvin Van Winkle, of Alliance.

Mr. David Webb, of Chillicothe, who is steeped in Ohio lore, especially about place names. He helped me with many of the stories around his section, particularly with "Tom Corwin," the "Sky-Foogle," and others.

Mr. Ernest J. Wessen, of Mansfield, a rare man and a fine scholar. He sells books, but, what is more important, he has an extraordinary knowledge of what is inside Ohio books.

When I decided to use "A Deer Trick," which I had heard sketchily from Reverend Crist of Lima and found also in Samuel Edwards' *The Ohio Hunters*, I asked Mr. Wessen what he knew about Edwards. His reply was that he knew "many oldsters who knew him . . . and relatives and youthful companions of his later years . . ." and found that "he [Edwards] was a fine, simple character, who simply told his story as it happened." I could not go any farther to authenticate the story.

Ohio abounds with stories about Tom Corwin, some real, and some attributed to him. The story I have used, and which Miss L. R. McCabe mentions in *Don't You Remember?*, and on which Dave Webb helped me, is also attributed to Abe Lincoln.

I found the charming "American Noodle Story" of "A Mr. Johnston" in Henry Howe's Historic Collection of Ohio. There are other versions of this tale in other counties.

Here are the folks of Indiana who made these stories possible:

Miss Helen C. Beatty, of Logansport.

Miss C. R. Berry, of Vincennes, whose collection of French folk songs of Vincennes is probably the best there is. She helped me unstintingly in my search for stories of her county.

Mr. W. E. Billings, North Manchester newspaperman, author, and storyteller, who knows enough lore about the Hoosier State to make up several volumes. He gave me many stories, but space permitted use of only two, "Why the Devil Keeps Out of Indiana," and "The Little *Prairie Hen* and the *Big Indiana*."

Mrs. Martha C. Bishop, a fine storyteller and author in her own right.

Mrs. Wyckoff Bottorff, of Charlestown. Mrs. Avis Brown, of Crown Point.

Dr. Grover Brown, Superintendent of Schools of Nashville, a magnificent storyteller.

Mrs. Avis Brown, of Crown Point.

Dr. R. C. Buley, Professor of History, Indiana University, in Bloomington, who has written rich histories, in which can be found lore as well, which is right and proper.

Miss Nellie Coats of the Indiana State Library. No words of thanks are adequate to express my gratitude for the generous help she gave me in my research.

Miss E. Cox, of Martinsville.

Miss L. Davis, of Salem. Mr. David I. Day, of Dale.

Miss Caroline Dunn, of the William Henry Smith Memorial Library, Indianapolis, a scholar and a very genius in research into the lore and history in her state. She gave me a great deal of material, told me many drolleries, and helped me with "Georgie Goes A-Sparkin' " and "The Colonel's Blanket."

Mrs. J. T. Force, of Shoals, helped me with the story of "The Miracle Flame." Her father, Mr. Carlos T. McCarty, is responsible for the story, and Mrs. Force states that it is unquestionably an authentic incident told by word of mouth. It appeared in print in the *Indiana Magazine of History*, Vol. X.

Mrs. A. R. Gentry, of Rockport. Mr. H. C. Gray, of Indianapolis.

Mrs. Leola Hocket, of Wabash, who aided me with Ohio history, including the boat-race story of "The Little *Prairie Hen* and the *Big Indiana*." The saga of that famous race is well known and is still told along the banks of the Wabash.

Mrs. Hazel W. Hopper, of the Indiana State Library, Indianapolis.

Mrs. Carl W. Johnson, of the Indiana State Library.

Professor Phillip Jordan, University of Minnesota, a fine storyteller and author. The story of "The Hat in the Moon" I heard first in Muncie on a warm summer's night when many other stories were being told. It was apparently a well-known story in many counties, and quite a few teachers knew it. Then, in going through Indiana books, I found it in Professor Jordan's scholarly and well written *The National Road*, giving the names of the characters. With his kind permission, I am using the same names.

Mrs. Josephine Draim Osmun, Mrs. Martha Ann Hanum, and Mrs. Emma Sies, three remarkable sisters, in their seventies and eighties, who live together in Vincennes. They told many stories, including the latter half of the Vincennes story.

Mrs. Frances S. C. Rawles, of Fort Wayne. Mrs. M. A. Rubins, of the Indiana State Library, in Indianapolis.

Mr. Lewis B. Richardson, of Trafalgar, poet and author, with a splendid knowledge of the lore of his state. He gave me enough stories to fill a book, and my regret is that I could not use them all. Here are those I used: "God's Own Country"—this is a type found with slight variations in every state; "The Sad Tale of Tom the Catfish," another story found in many states—the only variation is the type of fish to whom the tragedy happens; "Old Man Edmonds and the Ninety-nine Pigs." The stories of Old Man Edmonds are popular in Johnson County as well as all over Indiana. (There have been both studies and collections of them in the Hoosier Folklore Magazine.) Mr. Richardson knew Edmonds. He also told me the story of the "Copperhead in the Bin."

Mrs. Rose D. Schultheis, of Vincennes. Mrs. H. E. Shelley, of New Castle.

Judge Curtis Shake, of Vincennes, told me the Adam Gimbel story. It is a well-known tale in that section.

Mrs. F. Smith, of Delphi.

Mr. O. C. Toner, of Martinsville, told me the Lincoln story, which is well known. Mr. Louis Warren, Director of the Lincoln National Life Foundation in Fort Wayne, has been trying to find the origin of the story. So far he has been unsuccessful.

Miss Rose Valley, of Vincennes, who sang old French songs for me and told old French tales about Vincennes.

Miss Ethel A. Vinnedge, of Vincennes.

Mrs. Harry T. Watts, of the Old Post Association in Vincennes.

Mr. Louis A. Warren, of the Lincoln National Life Foundation, in Fort Wayne.

Mr. William J. Walter, ninety-nine years old, of Battle Ground, who told me some delightful tall tales "of his own life."

Mr. Elmer R. Waters, of Lafayette, with whom I spent a memorable evening in his art-museum-home swapping tales and hearing stories about Indiana that were a delight. Only lack of space prevents me from using them.

Mr. Sam B. Woods, of Griffith Lake County, is a page out of American life that is gone. Mr. Woods was ninety-three when he gave me the story of "Gentlin' the Ram," and many more besides. Mr. Woods said, "Have seen more changes in a lifetime than most of 'em," and he could fill volumes that would be truly early Americana.

Here are the sources of the Illinois stories:

Mr. Paul M. Angle, of Chicago.

Mr. O. L. Brown, of Vandalia.

Mr. Virginius H. Chase, of Peoria Heights.

Mr. E. L. Dukes, of Albion, author and folklorist, has written an excellent history of the county and its lore. He gave me many stories, including "The White Mule from the Other World."

Miss Inez Dunn, of the McLean County Historical Society in Bloomington.

It is impossible to escape stories about Peter Cartwright the moment you ask Illinois folks about their great men. I heard many of them talk about this colorful preacher who could fight as hard as he could preach. The story used in this book is mentioned by Mrs. Grant in her volume on Peter Cartwright, and Mr. Meine mentions it in his fine study of the Riverman under "secondary sources."

Mr. E. E. East, State Archival Assistant, who, along with his great knowledge of things historical, is also an expert on catfish, and so, naturally, had a word about the story of Illinois Catfish.

Miss Myrtis Evans, of Peoria, who was most co-operative and helped with a great deal of material dealing with the lore of Illinois.

Rushville, Illinois, has a few cannon stories to its credit, and the one I used is so full of good, colty Americanism that it had to be told once again in "The Governor and the Cannon."

Mrs. Stanley Hubbs, of Chicago, a folklorist and historian with personal "family" knowledge of history and lore. It is a pity that space prevents me from using her stories.

Mr. Johnson, of Peoria. Mrs. C. D. Jones, of LeRoy. Miss Mary S. King, of Winnetka.

The story of Preacher Lee and the butting lamb I heard when I was with a group of librarians in New York City and we were swapping tales. I subsequently also found it in *Pioneers of Menard and Mason Counties*, by T. G. Onstot (1902).

Mrs. M. H. Lyon, Jr., of Rock Island.

Lincoln stories in Illinois are as numerous as leaves on a hickory. Dr. Chandler was a highly respected settler, and the story of how he employed Lincoln as his surveyor actually happened. I heard the tale sketchily, and found it also in William H. Perrin's *History of Cass County* (1882).

Mr. David S. McIntosh, of Carbondale.

Miss N. S. Martin, of Princeville, whose greatgrandfather was probably Assessor Payne in "The Good Dog and the Good Assessor." She helped me in trying to track down the story.

Mrs. G. T. Millhouse, Jr., of the Galena Historical Document

Association. Mr. J. Monaghan, State Historian, of Springfield.

Mr. F. J. Meine, scholar and folklorist, for his valuable suggestions and leads.

Mrs. Marie Melberg, of the West Side Historical Society, in Chicago, who helped generously with many stories, among them, "The Dance at Hickory Creek."

"The Miller and the Blue Jay" story I found in William A. Perrin's *History of Jefferson County* (1883).

Mrs. Guyla Moreland, poet, columnist, farmer, and about a thousand and one other things which make her as amazing as a character in the Arabian Nights. She gave me much material, including help with these stories: "Sand in the Bag," "Giant Skeeters in the Brass Pot," and "All's Well That Ends Well."

Miss Adaline Naught, of Rushville, who related many incidents of early American life.

Mrs. Viola B. Neeson, of Chicago.

Mrs. B. W. Perkins, of Vandalia.

Mr. H. E. Pratt, State Historian, who gave me information and aid with the story on how Springfield became county seat.

Miss Mabel Richmond, of Decatur.

Mr. J. C. Sanders, of Chicago. Mrs. G. P. Smith, of Carbondale. Mrs. S. M. Snyder, of Metamora. Mr. Harry L. Spooner, of Peoria. Mrs. W. B. Wells, of St. Charles. Mr. G. Y. Williamson, of El Paso.

There were many others who helped me. They told me anecdotes that are gems and stories that should be in this book, but, alas, a book has a limited number of pages. But even if their names are not here in print, my thanks to them are just as sincere.

My deepest gratitude goes to Professor William Utter, of Denison University in Ohio, for generously saying something about these stories.

I also want to thank my wife for her patient and tireless research, and Nancy Hosking and Evelyn Shrifte for their helpful criticism. Finally I want to thank the members of Rooms 300 and 328 of the New York City Public Library for their most generous aid in my research in the library.

M. A. J.